wqe | Wyggeston &
Queen Elizabeth
College

Learn

GC

Science

David Chaundy
David Moore
Jane Taylor

Editor: Nigel Collins

ESSENTIAL WORD
DICTIONARY

Philip Allan Updates
Market Place
Deddington
Oxfordshire
OX15 0SE

tel: 01869 338652
fax: 01869 337590
e-mail: sales@philipallan.co.uk
www.philipallan.co.uk

Printed by Raithby, Lawrence & Co Ltd, Leicester

Introduction

This is a concise dictionary of key terms used in GCSE courses in Double Award Science. It covers the content of both Coordinated Science and Modular Science specifications. Each word has been carefully chosen and is explained in detail to enhance your knowledge and understanding of science.

In the dictionary, each word is defined in up to four parts, as follows.
- a brief definition
- further explanation of the word
- an example
- an examiner's tip, such as where a word is commonly misunderstood, confused with another word, used in error, or found in conjunction with other words in the dictionary

In many cases, all four parts are not needed and the entry has been amended accordingly. Finally, for each term it may be necessary to make a cross-reference to the words in italics in order to understand fully the entry you are reading.

Overleaf you will find tables of multiples and sub-multiples, Greek symbols, some useful conversion factors and equivalent units, as well as symbols used in electronic circuits.

Make extensive use of this 'essential words' dictionary. It could provide a significant boost to your chances of success in GCSE Science.

Multiples and sub-multiples

tera	T	10^{12}
giga	G	10^9
mega	M	10^6
kilo	k	10^3
deci	d	10^{-1}
centi	c	10^{-2}
milli	m	10^{-3}
micro	μ	10^{-6}
nano	n	10^{-9}
pico	p	10^{-12}
femto	f	10^{-15}
atto	a	10^{-18}

Some Greek symbols

α	alpha
β	beta
γ	gamma
δ	delta
λ	lambda
π	pi
ρ	rho
μ	mu
θ	theta
ω/Ω	omega

Imperial equivalents

1 inch = 2.54 cm exactly
1 mile = 1.609 km
1 mile per hour = 0.447 m/s
1 gallon = 4.55 dm^3
1 ounce = 28.3 g
1 pound = 0.454 kg
1 horsepower = 746 W
1 acre = 0.4047 hectare

Circuit symbols

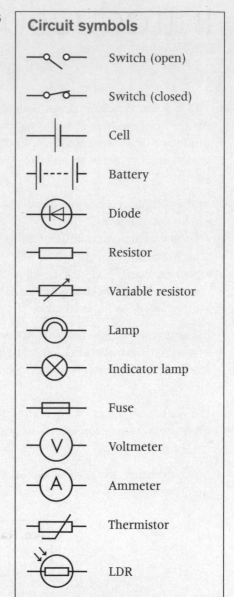

Switch (open)	
Switch (closed)	
Cell	
Battery	
Diode	
Resistor	
Variable resistor	
Lamp	
Indicator lamp	
Fuse	
Voltmeter	
Ammeter	
Thermistor	
LDR	

Metric units

1 litre = 1000 cm^3 = 1 dm^3
1 hectare = 10^4 m^2
1 standard atmosphere = the pressure of 760 mm of mercury
$\qquad\qquad\qquad\quad$ = 101.3 N/m^2
1 bar = 10^5 N/m^2

WQEIC LRC

absolute zero: the lowest possible temperature; 0 *kelvin*, −273°C.
■ In laboratories, scientists have produced temperatures only a fraction of a degree above absolute zero.

a.c.: see *alternating current*.

acceleration: the rate of change of *velocity*; that is, the change of velocity divided by the time taken.
■ *e.g.* A car slows from 10 m/s to 2 m/s in 4 seconds. The acceleration is
$$\frac{(2-10)\,\text{m/s}}{4\,\text{s}} = -2\,\text{m/s}^2$$

TIP Acceleration can be a change in direction at a steady speed as well as a change in speed or velocity.

acceleration/time graph: a graph that shows how the acceleration of an object, plotted vertically, varies with time, plotted horizontally.
■ The area under the graph gives the change of speed.

acetic acid: see *ethanoic acid*.

a.c. generator (also called 'alternator')**:** an electric *generator* that produces alternating current.
■ An a.c. generator usually has fixed coils. These may surround a rotating magnet or, in larger machines, a rotating coil carrying a direct current. This rotating coil is connected by *slip rings* to a source of *direct current*.

acid: a substance that can donate H^+ ions when in solution to give a *pH* of less than 7.
■ Substances that donate many H^+ ions are called strong acids; those that donate few ions are called weak acids. Acids turn blue litmus paper red, and react with bases.
■ *e.g.* Sulphuric, nitric and hydrochloric acids are strong acids; ethanoic and oxalic acids are weak acids.

1

acid rain: rainfall that has absorbed acidic gases (such as sulphur dioxide and nitrogen dioxide — both of which are by-products of the combustion of *fossil fuels,* including petrol in car engines and oil or coal in power stations). Its *pH* is normally less than 5.3.

■Acid rain may cause damage to buildings and statues and may affect water courses as well as plant and animal life. It is also involved in *weathering* of rocks. Rainfall is normally slightly acidic due to dissolved carbon dioxide from the air.

activated charcoal: charcoal that has been dried and powdered so that it is very porous and has a large surface area.

■It can be used for adsorbing impurities from either gases or liquids. It is widely used in gas masks and is also used to remove the colour from sugar solutions before they are crystallised to make table sugar.

active immunity: immunity that develops after encountering microorganisms or fragments of foreign material. *Antibodies* that stick to the microorganism are made by the *immune system,* and the body keeps a permanent memory of the infection.

■The permanent memory is held by the cells which divide and release antibodies very quickly in the face of future infections by the same microorganism. In *vaccination* the immune system is provoked to make antibodies and memory cells by a microbe (or its components) in a vaccine.

active site: the part of an *enzyme* molecule that is involved in the reaction it catalyses.

■The substance(s) involved in the reaction fit into the active site. The 3D shape of the enzyme and its active site changes with pH and high temperatures.

active transport: the process of moving substances into or out of a cell using *energy.*

■Energy is supplied by *respiration* in the cells concerned. Active transport can move substances against a concentration gradient.

■ *e.g.* Root hair cells import potassium ions from the soil. Kidney tubule cells use active transport to reabsorb glucose from the fluid passing through them so that it is not lost in urine.

adaptation: the possession of features that enhance an organism's ability to survive in its habitat.

■Animals and plants may have physical features, physiological abilities or behaviour patterns that allow them to cope with the particular difficulties of their environment and mode of life.

■ *e.g.* Animals living in cold environments have thick coats; desert-dwelling kangaroo rats can reabsorb large amounts of water from their kidney tubules.

addiction: a state of being dependent on a *drug,* in which the individual feels a need to take the drug regularly.

■ Some drugs induce physical dependency, and an individual suffers withdrawal symptoms if the drug is not available. Other drugs cause psychological dependency where the individual experiences cravings but does not get withdrawal symptoms.

■ *e.g.* Heroin and nicotine form physical dependencies.

addition reaction: a reaction in which two substances react together to make one product.

■ This is a common reaction of *alkenes*, for example the addition of water to ethene to make ethanol.

adrenaline: a chemical in the body which acts as both a *hormone* and a *neuro-transmitter*.

aerobic respiration: *respiration* in the presence of oxygen.

■ This involves the complete oxidation of glucose to CO_2 and H_2O, with a relatively large release of energy compared with *anaerobic respiration*.

alcohol: an organic compound that contains the $-OH$ group.

■ Alcohols are used as solvents in industry.

■ *e.g.* Examples are methanol (CH_3OH), ethanol (C_2H_5OH), propanol (C_3H_7OH) and butanol (C_4H_9OH). Ethanol is found in alcoholic beverages and is also used in some countries as a fuel for cars.

aldehyde: an organic compound that contains the CHO group.

■ Aldehydes have a fruity smell. They are produced by the oxidation of *alcohols*. They can be oxidised further to carboxylic acids.

algal bloom: the rapid growth of single-celled algae and blue-green bacteria in water under favourable conditions, to the extent that they colour the water.

■ Algal growth is limited by the amounts of minerals available in the water. *Fertiliser* and water treatment works can boost the amounts of nitrate and phosphate that drain into water. In the warmer parts of the year algae reproduce faster than they are eaten and the numbers are high enough to block light transmission through water. This can lead to *eutrophication*.

alkali: a substance that produces OH^- ions in solution.

■ Alkaline solutions have a *pH* greater than 7. Alkalis can be strong (form many OH^- ions in solution), such as sodium hydroxide, or weak (form few OH^- ions in solution), such as sodium hydrogencarbonate.

■ Alkalis turn red litmus paper to blue. They have a soapy feel when in solution.

alkali metal: the common name for any of the elements in group 1 in the periodic table — lithium, sodium, potassium, rubidium, caesium and francium.

■ They all have one electron in their outermost electronic shell. They are reactive metals whose reactivity increases down the group. Alkali metals are extracted

a

by the *electrolysis* of their molten salts. They form ionic compounds that are usually soluble in water.

alkaline earth metal: the common name for any of the group 2 elements in the periodic table — beryllium, magnesium, calcium, strontium, barium and radium.

■ They all have two electrons in their outermost electronic shell. They are reactive metals whose reactivity increases down the group. Alkaline earth metals are extracted by the *electrolysis* of their molten salts.

alkane: the general term for a class of compounds made up of carbon and hydrogen atoms only and which have only carbon–carbon single bonds.

■ Alkanes have the general formula C_nH_{2n+2}. They are generally unreactive, although they will usually burn in air and undergo substitution reactions with *halogens* in the presence of ultraviolet light.

alkene: the general term for a class of compounds made up of carbon and hydrogen atoms only and which have one or more carbon–carbon double bonds.

■ They have the general formula C_nH_{2n}. Alkenes are quite reactive and will readily undergo addition reactions either with themselves (to make *polymers*) or with other compounds. They will usually burn in air to produce carbon dioxide and water.

allele: one of the forms of a particular gene. Alleles are carried as pairs, one on each of a pair of *chromosomes*.

■ Genes control a particular characteristic, such as height of a pea plant; alleles control different versions of the characteristic, such as tall or short plants. Similarly, free or attached earlobes are determined by different alleles.

TIP

Some genes have several alleles, for example A, B or O blood group alleles. In some textbooks you may find the term 'gene' used instead of 'allele'.

allotrope: an element that can exist in two or more different forms due to the arrangement of its atoms.

■ *e.g.* Carbon has three different allotropes: diamond, graphite and buckminsterfullerene.

alloy: a substance made by mixing a metal with one or more other metals or non-metals.

■ Alloys generally have different properties from their constituent metals.

■ *e.g.* Steel (iron and carbon), brass (copper and zinc) and pewter (tin and lead).

alluvial: matter that has been washed along by rivers and streams and then deposited — usually at a river mouth.

■ It consists of small pebbles, rocks and fine-grained material. Alluvial material makes good farmland as it is rich in minerals.

alpha particle: a positively charged particle (a helium nucleus with 2 *protons* and 2 *neutrons*) ejected from the nuclei of some radioactive atoms during the process of radioactive *decay*. Alpha particles are highly ionising but can travel only a few centimetres in air and are easily stopped by paper or thin metal.

TIP The greater the ionisation, the easier it is to stop the radiation.

alternating current (a.c.): an electric current that keeps changing direction.
■ Mains electricity throughout Britain alternates at a frequency of 50 cycles per second (*hertz*).

alternator: see *a.c. generator.*

aluminium: a silvery metal found in group 3 of the periodic table.
■ Aluminium conducts heat and electricity well and is not very dense. It is widely used in *alloys* — particularly in the aircraft industry. Although high in the reactivity series it is generally not reactive due to a protective oxide coating that forms on its surface. It is extracted from the mineral *bauxite* (Al_2O_3) by *electrolysis*.

alveolus (pl. alveoli)**:** a minute cavity at the end of an airway in the lungs where gas exchange takes place.
■ *Capillaries* run alongside alveoli, bringing blood from the body tissues. Oxygen passes into the blood from the alveolar air and carbon dioxide leaves the blood. Each alveolus has a large surface area and very thin walls, only one cell thick, to maximise gas exchange.

amino acid: the sub-unit used to make protein molecules.
■ Plants make amino acids from nitrate and glucose. Animals obtain amino acids by digesting proteins in food. Humans need a mixture of the 20 naturally occurring amino acids to make human proteins. Essential amino acids can only be supplied by the food we eat but we can convert some surplus amino acids into others if necessary. Amino acids are broken down in the liver to make *urea*, and excreted by the kidneys in *urine*.

ammeter: a meter that measures electric *currents*. It may be *analogue*, with a moving pointer, or *digital*, with a numerical display.

TIP Ammeters are always connected in a *series circuit* and have a low *resistance*. First break the circuit and then connect the ammeter across the gap.

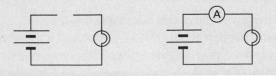

ammonia: a pungent colourless gas (NH_3).

■ Ammonia is formed naturally by bacteria decomposing proteins and urea. It is manufactured by the combination of nitrogen (from the air) and hydrogen (from steam and methane) in the presence of a *catalyst* of iron (the Haber process). Ammonia is highly soluble in water. It is used to make cleaning agents, nitric acid and fertilisers. Ammonium compounds contain the NH_4^+ ion, and are also soluble in water.

amp: common abbreviation of *ampere*.

ampere: the unit of electric *current*, symbol A. 1 ampere is a flow of 1 *coulomb* per second.

amplitude: the height of a *wave*; the maximum displacement of any oscillation or *sound wave* from the rest position.

TIP

Measuring the height from a crest to a trough gives twice the amplitude.

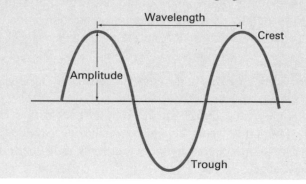

anaerobic respiration: the process of releasing energy from food without using oxygen.

■ Yeast releases carbon dioxide and ethanol from this process but human muscle cells produce lactic acid which contributes to the *oxygen debt*. Less of the energy in glucose is released in anaerobic respiration than in *aerobic respiration*.

analogue: something that varies steadily to correspond with an input signal. Compare *digital*.

■ *e.g.* The pointer of an analogue meter moves steadily to show the *voltage* or *current* being measured. In radio transmission the amplitude or the frequency of a radio or television signal varies according to the sound or picture brightness being transmitted. (Hence a.m. — amplitude modulation — and f.m. — frequency modulation — radio stations.)

anhydrous: describing substances that contain no water.

■ *e.g.* Hydrated copper sulphate ($CuSO_4.5H_2O$) is blue, but if the water is removed by heating, anhydrous copper sulphate ($CuSO_4$) is produced which is white. This process is reversible.

anion: an atom or group of atoms that has gained one or more electrons.
■ Anions are formed during the making of an *ionic bond*.
■ *e.g.* Chloride (Cl^-) and sulphate ions (SO_4^{2-}) are examples of anions.

anode: the positive electrode in *electrolysis*.

anodising: the process of thickening the oxide coating on a piece of aluminium by making it the anode in an electrochemical cell containing dilute sulphuric acid.
■ The thickened film protects the aluminium better and is able to incorporate dyes when the metal is coloured for decorative purposes.

antagonistic muscles: muscles that work in opposition to each other.
■ Antagonistic muscles move joints; one muscle contracts to flex the joint and the other contracts to extend it again.
■ *e.g.* The elbow joint is moved by a pair of antagonistic muscles. The biceps flexes the arm and the triceps extends it.

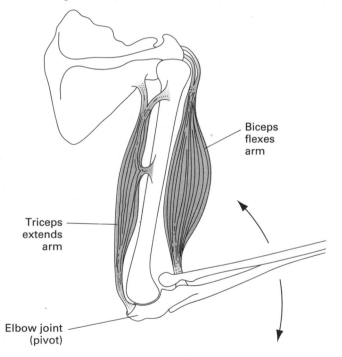

Biceps
flexes
arm

Triceps
extends
arm

Elbow joint
(pivot)

antibiotic: a substance produced by a microbe that kills or stops the growth of other microbes.
■ Most commercially available antibiotics are made by fungi or bacteria. Each is effective against a particular group of infectious bacteria and is used to treat infections.
■ *e.g.* Penicillin is produced by the fungus ***Penicillium***.

a

antibody: a *protein* in the blood that attaches to foreign material, such as *microbes* and transplanted organs, that has entered the body tissues. See *immune system*.
- Antibodies are made by *B-lymphocytes*. They stick to microbes and hinder their activity. They mark microbes and foreign material for destruction by other white cells in the blood. A different antibody is needed for each variety of microbe.

anticline: an upwards, convex bulge of sedimentary rock strata within the *crust* of the Earth.
- In oil-bearing regions, geologists look for anticlines as oil and gas may be trapped beneath them.
- The opposite of an anticline is a *syncline*.

antidiuretic hormone (ADH): a *hormone* secreted by the brain which is involved in controlling the water balance of the body.
- ADH is secreted into the blood when the brain detects a lowering concentration of water in the blood. It causes the kidneys to reabsorb more water, which results in a more concentrated urine. ADH secretion is reduced when the water content of the blood increases, so that less water is reabsorbed in the kidneys.

antigen: a substance found in cell membranes and cell walls that triggers a reaction by the *immune system*.
- Antigens on microbes and foreign materials in the body provoke the production of *antibodies* by specialised white cells. *White blood cells* destroy cells with antibodies stuck to their antigens. This causes problems for transplants because the transplanted organ carries the donor's antigens; if they are different from the recipient's antigens the recipient's immune system will try to destroy this 'foreign object'. Tissue transplants are most successful when the donor and recipient have very closely matching antigens.

aorta: the main vessel carrying oxygen-rich blood from the left side of the heart to the body.
- The aorta has strong elastic walls which enable it to stretch and accommodate the surge of blood from the heart with each beat, helping to smooth out the supply to the tissues. The exit from the heart into the aorta has a valve that stops blood from returning to the heart when the pressure drops at the end of each beat. The sound of the valve closing can be heard with a stethoscope.

aqueous: describes solutions that consist of a substance that has been dissolved in water.
- In equations an aqueous solution is represented by the symbol (aq).

area under a graph: the result of multiplying the *x* variable by the *y* variable for the given graph, taking account of the way the height of the graph changes.
- *e.g.* The area under a *speed/time graph* gives the distance travelled. The area under an *acceleration/time graph* gives the change in speed.

TIP

Be careful here. This graph could be showing speed (y) plotted vertically against time (x) plotted horizontally. The area under the graph would therefore show distance (speed × time). In the triangular part of the graph, the distance travelled would be $\frac{1}{2}yx$. In the rectangular part of the graph, the distance travelled would be yx.

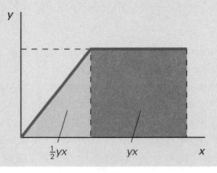

argon: one of the noble gases found in group 8 of the periodic table.

■ Argon has a full outer shell of electrons and so is unreactive towards other elements. It is extracted from the air (0.9%) by fractional distillation. Argon is used to fill light bulbs, as a protective atmosphere during welding, and is bubbled through molten iron to stir it during the steel-making process.

armature: the rotating part of an electric *motor* or *generator*. It contains one or more coils of wire, an iron core and, in d.c. machines, a *commutator*.

artery: a blood vessel that carries blood away from the heart to an organ or tissue.

■ The walls are thick and elastic to accommodate the high-pressure surge of blood accompanying each heartbeat. Muscle fibres in the walls can change an artery's diameter to increase or reduce the blood supply to an organ according to the body's needs.

■ *e.g.* *Vasodilation* increases the amount of blood flowing to the skin to help cool the body.

asexual reproduction: production of offspring without the use of specialised sex cells or genetic change.

■ This is common in microorganisms and plants, as well as some animals. It allows them to colonise favourable environments quickly. One parent organism produces offspring that are identical both to the parent and to each other, forming a *clone*. Single-celled organisms use *binary fission*, in which one cell splits to become two. Plants generate small plantlets, bulbs, corms and tubers which root and eventually live independently. See also *vegetative propagation*.

■ *e.g.* Aphids — greenfly and blackfly — reproduce asexually at one stage in their life cycle. In this way, females produce offspring very quickly in late spring and summer.

a

assimilation: the process of absorbing materials from the gut and incorporating them into cells.

■ Some materials absorbed from the gut are not assimilated. Surplus *amino acids* are broken down in the liver and part of each molecule excreted as *urea* in urine.

asteroid: one of many rocky objects that *orbit* the Sun between the orbits of Mars and Jupiter.

atmosphere: the mixture of gases that surrounds a planet. These gases are prevented from escaping by the pull of gravity.

■ The Earth's atmosphere consists of 78% nitrogen, 21% oxygen, 0.9% argon and 0.03% carbon dioxide. There are also other gases present, such as water vapour and the noble gases.

■ *e.g.* Gases within the atmosphere help to keep the Earth warm and to prevent harmful rays from the Sun from reaching the surface of the Earth.

atom: the smallest part of an element that still retains the properties of that element.

■ Atoms consist of a very small but heavy *nucleus* of *protons* (positively charged) and *neutrons* (no charge) surrounded by *electrons* (negatively charged) orbiting in shells, rather like planets around the Sun. In a neutral atom there are the same number of protons as electrons. Different elements have different numbers of protons in the nucleus within the atom.

atomic lattice: the regular three-dimensional arrangement of atoms within a crystal.

■ The atoms are packed closely together.

atomic mass: the unit used to measure the relative mass of an atom or molecule.

■ Masses are compared with $\frac{1}{12}$ of the mass of an atom of carbon-12. The mass of an atom or molecule is primarily due to the numbers of protons and neutrons present, as the mass of electrons is negligible.

atomic number (also called 'proton number')**:** the number of protons within the nucleus of an atom. In a neutral atom, this is the same as the number of orbiting electrons.

■ No two elements have the same atomic number.

■ *e.g.* Carbon has an atomic number of 6, and sodium has one of 11.

ATP (adenosine triphosphate): A store of chemical energy within cells, used as the immediate source of energy for chemical reactions. It is made during respiration when glucose is broken down.

attraction: the *force* between any two *masses* (gravitational), between unlike magnetic poles (magnetic) and between unlike electric charges (*electrostatic*).

auxin: a plant growth substance involved in the control of growth and in the plant's response to light.

▨ There are several auxins. The most common is IAA (indole acetic acid). Auxin is produced in shoot tips and diffuses downwards. It has several effects, including promoting cell elongation and cell division so that shoots lengthen. At high concentrations it inhibits side buds on a shoot.

▨ *e.g.* Auxin preparation is used to help cuttings root. Gardeners can grow bushier plants by pinching the tips off shoots, removing the source of auxin, so the side buds will grow. A synthetic auxin (2,4-D) disrupts a plant's growth and is used as a weedkiller.

Avogadro's constant: see *Avogadro's number.*

Avogadro's number (also called 'Avogadro's constant'): the number of particles present in one mole of a substance.

▨ Avogadro's number has a numerical value of 6.02×10^{23}.

▨ *e.g.* One mole of argon atoms (40 g) and one mole of water molecules (18 g) each contain Avogadro's number of particles.

axon: a long, thin extension of a *nerve cell* that conducts a nerve impulse towards the next cell.

▨ An axon can be short or very long, for example extending from the spine to the end of a limb. In some nerve cells a sheath of fatty material, called myelin, helps speed up the passage of the impulse along the axon. Clusters of axons form nerves.

background radiation: the low level of radiation that is always present. (See *radiation, nuclear.*)

■ Background radiation comes from such things as rocks, food, air, buildings and outer space. (See *cosmic radiation.*)

In any radioactive measurements the background radiation should be subtracted from the observed count.

bacterium: a single-celled organism consisting of cytoplasm and a membrane surrounded by a cell wall. The genetic material is not in a distinct nucleus but loose in the cytoplasm.

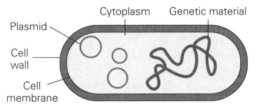

■ Bacteria are important *microbes* because they cause disease, food spoilage and decomposition. They are involved in nutrient cycling (see *carbon cycle* and *nitrogen cycle*). They are also used in genetic modification.

baking powder: the common name for a mixture of chemicals of which the primary component is sodium hydrogencarbonate ($NaHCO_3$).

■ When heated, baking powder decomposes, giving off carbon dioxide. In the presence of acids carbon dioxide is also formed. When used in cooking, the carbon dioxide liberated forms bubbles within the mixture which 'rises'.

balanced forces: equal and opposite forces on an object in *equilibrium*. These allow the object to remain at rest or to continue to move in a straight line at a steady speed.

■ **e.g.** When you stand on the floor, your *weight* is balanced by the upward force of the floor on your feet.

barometer: an instrument for measuring the *pressure* of the atmosphere.
- Some barometers have a column of mercury about 760 mm tall. In aneroid (no liquid) barometers the atmospheric pressure compresses an evacuated box against the force of a spring.

basalt: a dark-coloured rock composed of tiny interlocking crystals, formed when molten *igneous rock,* expelled from volcanoes, cools quickly on the surface of the Earth.

base, chemical: a substance that can neutralise an acid to form a salt.
- Bases are proton (H⁺) acceptors. Those that are soluble in water (e.g. ammonia) are called alkalis.
- *e.g.* Copper oxide and manganese dioxide.

base-pairing: the specific linking of bases in *DNA* to particular partner bases because of the structure of their molecules.
- Adenine (A) can only pair with thymine (T) while cytosine (C) pairs with guanine (G).

bases, ATCG: a group of subunits making up *DNA* molecules.
- DNA molecules contain many thousands of bases. They are attached to the sugar–phosphate 'backbone' strands of the DNA molecule. Each base on one strand links to a corresponding base on the other, linking the two strands together like the rungs of a ladder. There are four types of base: adenine (A), cytosine (C), guanine (G) and thymine (T). (See *base-pairing.*)

battery (also called 'electrical cell'): two or more electrochemical cells connected in series to provide higher voltages of direct current.
- An electrochemical cell usually consists of a metal in contact with a solution (the electrolyte). When two cells with different metals are connected, chemical changes that occur between the metals and the electrolyte(s) result in an electrical current being able to flow when the electrodes are connected together in an electrical circuit. In a torch battery, the electrolyte solution is usually replaced by a moist paste — a so-called 'dry' battery.

TIP The *voltage* of the battery is the sum of the voltages of all the cells, provided they are all connected the same way round.

bauxite: the common name for the ore from which *aluminium* is extracted.
- It is mainly aluminium oxide, but also contains traces of iron oxide, sand and other minerals. The main source is in Jamaica. Bauxite has to be treated with sodium hydroxide to purify it before aluminium is extracted.

Benedict's solution: a chemical used to detect the presence of certain sugars in a solution.
- Benedict's solution is light blue in colour. A sample of test solution is mixed

with Benedict's solution and heated in a water bath at a temperature near boiling. If sugar is present, an orange-red precipitate gives the solution a brownish red colour.

Sucrose does not react in this way and so cannot be detected with this test.

benzene: an organic compound with the formula C_6H_6.
■ The carbon atoms are arranged in a six-membered ring. Although benzene is an *unsaturated compound*, it undergoes substitution reactions rather than addition reactions. It is obtained from the refining of crude oil and is used as a solvent and as a precursor for the manufacture of other chemicals.

beta particle: A fast-moving (about $\frac{9}{10}$ the speed of light) negative particle (*electron*) ejected from the nucleus of an atom when it undergoes radioactive *decay*.
■ The electron is formed by the breakdown of a *neutron* into a *proton* and an electron. Beta particles produce less *ionisation* than *alpha particles* but are more penetrating and can travel through air and skin. They are stopped by thick aluminium.

big bang: the great explosion that is thought to have started our *universe* 12 billion years ago.
■ The universe has been expanding ever since.

bile: a secretion, made by the liver and stored in the gall bladder before being discharged into the small intestine. It is involved in fat digestion.
■ Bile contains salts that act as an emulsifier and detergent, breaking up globules of fat in food into smaller droplets. This gives a larger surface area for fat-digesting enzymes to work on and assists absorption in the small intestine. It also contains breakdown products from old red blood cells destroyed in the liver. Bile helps to neutralise acid entering the small intestine from the stomach.

binary fission: a form of *asexual reproduction*.
■ A cell makes a copy of its genes and divides into two equal halves that become two new cells. This is the main method of reproduction in bacteria.

bioaccumulation: a process in which a potentially harmful substance is taken into organisms in the early levels of a food chain and passes to organisms further along the chain in increasing amounts.
■ The substance is not broken down or excreted; instead it accumulates within organisms in increasing quantities. Organisms at the start of the chain may not take in enough for harmful effects, but organisms further along the food chain accumulate more as they continue to take in food items. Levels in predatory animals high in the food chain may reach harmful quantities.
■ *e.g.* Some *pesticides* applied to crops may enter food chains and accumulate in harmful quantities in predatory birds.

b

biodiversity: a term used to describe the richness and variety of species in a habitat.

■ Expanding farming and fishing areas and the exploitation of natural forest products are leading to a loss in biodiversity in many habitats. Rare, specialist and less adaptable species are lost as their habitat is changed or destroyed.

biogas: a gaseous mixture consisting mainly of methane (CH_4) and carbon dioxide, formed by the controlled fermentation of waste plant and animal material.

■ Biogas is a renewable resource and an alternative to fossil fuels.

biological control: the use of a natural predator to reduce the number of pests infesting a crop.

■ Biological control can be a very specific method of controlling pests if the chosen predator attacks only the target pest and leaves other beneficial organisms alone. Predators are slower acting than chemical pesticides and will not eliminate pests. However, they can reduce the numbers significantly, they reproduce themselves for free and do not leave chemical residues on food crops.

■ *e.g.* Parasitic wasps can be used to control white flies in greenhouses. The wasps lay their eggs in the white flies. Nematode worms can be used to control slugs in a garden.

biomass: the total *dry mass* of a population of animals or plants.

■ Biomass is used in ecological studies to quantify the amount of living material at different positions in a food chain. Biomass allows fair comparisons to be made between organisms of different sizes.

TIP

When comparing two habitats, the biomass of one tree may equate to the biomass of several thousand grass plants.

biotechnology: industrial or commercial processes that use living organisms or their products to make a commodity.

■ Bacteria, fungi and the *enzymes* they make are widely used to make products such as vitamins, antibiotics, washing powder and vaccines. *Selective breeding* produces strains that are more efficient at doing the job. *Genetic modification* may be used to introduce new or more effective genes into bacteria and fungi.

■ *e.g.* Biotechnology includes *micropropagation* of plants. Beer, wine and food products such as cheese and yoghurt are also developed using biotechnology.

biuret test: a chemical test used to detect protein in a solution.

■ The test solution is made alkaline with sodium hydroxide, and dilute copper sulphate solution (pale blue) is added slowly. A lilac or purple colour indicates the presence of protein.

black dwarf: the final stage in the life of a *star* that has been a *white dwarf* and has contracted further.

b

black hole: a collapsed star that is so dense that neither matter nor light can escape from it.
- It could be the end stage of a *neutron star*.

blast furnace: a tall, tower-like structure used in the manufacture of iron from iron ore, limestone and coke.
- These raw materials are put in the top of the tower and hot air is blasted into the bottom. As a result of chemical reactions that occur within the tower, molten iron is formed which can be drained from the bottom periodically. The main reaction that occurs in the blast furnace is:

$$Fe_2O_3 + 3CO \longrightarrow 2Fe + 3CO_2$$

blood cells: see *red blood cell, white blood cell*.

blood clotting: a series of reactions resulting in the formation of a blood clot to seal small wounds.
- Fibrinogen is a protein carried in *plasma*. It is converted to insoluble strands of fibrin when a wound exposes the blood to air and a roughened surface. The strands form a loose mesh that traps red blood cells and forms a clot. Blood platelets carry factors that assist in this process. Haemophilia is an inherited condition in which a person fails to make one of the factors needed for blood clotting.

boiling point: the temperature at which vapour and liquid are in equilibrium, at atmospheric pressure.
- At boiling point, bubbles of vapour are seen to form within the liquid. As atmospheric pressure is decreased, so the boiling point decreases. Boiling points can be used to determine the purity of a liquid since impurities tend to elevate its boiling point.
- *e.g.* Pure water has a boiling point of 100°C at standard pressure.

bond: a force that holds atoms together within a molecule.
- Bonds can be *ionic bonds* due to the transfer of electrons, or *covalent bonds* due to the sharing of electrons. *Metallic bonds* are formed from a sea of electrons holding together the positive metal ions.

bond energy: the energy needed to break 1 *mole* of bonds.
- The same amount of energy is given out when 1 mole of these bonds forms. Bond energy is measured in kilojoules per mole of bonds (kJ/mol).
- *e.g.* For oxygen gas (O_2) the bond energy is 498 kJ/mol.

bromine: a member of the halogens (group 7 in the periodic table).
- Bromine has seven electrons in the outermost shell. It is a corrosive, volatile red liquid. Bromine is extracted from sea water and also from the Dead Sea. It is used in the manufacture of fire-retardant chemicals, fuel additives, pesticides and dyes.

b

bronze: an alloy made from copper (about 75%) and tin (about 25%).

■ Bronze is harder than either of its constituent metals and resists corrosion. It is used for machine parts and bell making. It was one of the earliest alloys known to man and as such gives its name to an era of pre-history (around 5000–1000 BC).

Brownian movement: the small, rapid, random movement of smoke particles in air or pollen grains suspended in water.

■ The movement is evidence that the smoke or pollen particles are being bombarded by even smaller molecules of air or water. The fact that the movement does not stop is good evidence for the *kinetic theory*.

brush: an electrical connector, usually made of carbon, that makes contact with the moving *slip ring* or *commutator* of a *motor* or *generator*.

burette: a long glass tube with a tap on the bottom that has been calibrated so that it can deliver accurately known amounts of liquid.

■ Commonly the burette will hold up to 50cm^3 of liquid, and volumes can be dispensed with an accuracy of 0.05cm^3.

burning: see *combustion*.

cable: insulated electrical conductors enclosed in an insulated outer sheath. (See *conductor, electrical*.)

■ *Mains electricity* cables have live conductors with brown insulation and neutral conductors with blue insulation. A third earth conductor (see *earth, electrical*) with green and yellow insulation is used unless the equipment has *double insulation*.

cable grip: the clamp that holds the *cable* in a mains plug and ensures that there is no strain on the terminals.

TIP It should grip the outer sheathing and not the insulation on the wires.

calcium carbonate: the chemical name for chalk, limestone or marble ($CaCO_3$).

■ Calcium carbonate is formed by the slow deposition of seashells in shallow seas over many millions of years. Heat and compaction cause it to fuse together. Caves are formed in limestone by the action of slightly acidic rain water dissolving the calcium carbonate. If calcium carbonate is heated it decomposes, forming calcium oxide and carbon dioxide.

capillary: a small blood vessel supplying cells with materials and removing wastes.

■ Capillaries are specialised for the exchange of materials between cells and blood. They have extremely thin walls, one cell thick, and branch repeatedly so that all cells are close to a capillary. Fluid carrying dissolved materials leaves the capillaries together with oxygen, minerals and nutrients such as glucose. Cells release carbon dioxide into the blood. The branching network of capillaries within a tissue makes a capillary bed. The branches eventually reunite to become venules, taking blood away from the tissues. Much of the fluid leaving the capillaries is returned to the blood by the end of the capillary bed.

carbohydrate: a compound found in animals and plants consisting of units of atoms of carbon, hydrogen and oxygen (CH_2O) linked together to make larger molecules.

■ Carbohydrates are used as an energy source by plants and animals, and also as a raw material for the synthesis of other substances. Glucose is the main energy source used by cells in *respiration*. Carbohydrates are stored as starch in plants and as glycogen in animals.

■ *e.g.* Glucose is a raw material for the production of *amino acids*, cellulose and fats.

carbon: an element occurring in group 4 of the periodic table, which is found in all *organic* compounds.

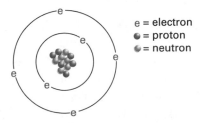

e = electron
● = proton
◐ = neutron

■ When combined with hydrogen, carbon forms the class of chemicals that are encompassed by the term 'organic chemistry'. This forms by far the largest number of compounds known.

■ *e.g.* Carbon can exist as three different *allotropes*: diamond, graphite and buckminsterfullerene. Diamond is commonly used in jewellery and for cutting implements while graphite is used as a lubricant and a conductor of electricity.

carbonate: an ion and an acid radical of formula CO_3^{2-}.

■ Carbonates form *salts* with metal ions. All carbonates give off carbon dioxide when added to acid. They are generally insoluble in water (except group 1). Most carbonates (not group 1) give off carbon dioxide when heated.

■ *e.g.* The most common carbonate is calcium carbonate ($CaCO_3$).

carbon cycle: the way in which carbon is circulated throughout the natural world.

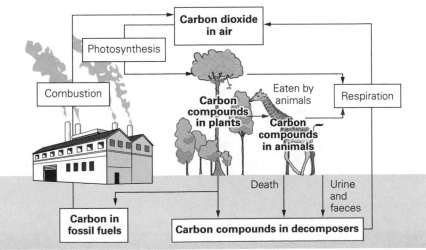

C

■ Carbon dioxide in the atmosphere is converted to sugars in plants by the process of photosynthesis. The accumulated carbon is returned to the atmosphere either by combustion, or from the plant being turned, over millions of years, into fossil fuels, which are then burned. Plants may also be eaten by animals. Carbon is returned to the air as carbon dioxide by respiration which occurs in all living things including decomposers which have eaten waste materials and dead organisms. Excessive use of fossil fuels, increasing the amount of carbon dioxide in the atmosphere, is upsetting the carbon cycle.

carbon dating (also called 'radiocarbon dating'): the dating of long-dead plants or animals by looking at the amount of radioactive carbon-14 they contain.

■ A very small proportion of the carbon dioxide in the atmosphere contains radioactive carbon-14. Living things take in this carbon, either by *photosynthesis* or by eating plants. Once the organism dies it stops taking in the radioactive carbon and the carbon starts to decay radioactively. By looking at the proportion of carbon-14 that remains, the age of the organism can be calculated.

carbon dioxide: a colourless, odourless gas produced whenever carbon-containing compounds are burned in air.

■ The atmosphere contains 0.03% carbon dioxide. It is taken in during *photosynthesis* and given out during *respiration*. It does not support combustion and is denser than air. It is also formed when acid is added to carbonates and hydrogencarbonates. It is used in fire-extinguishers and as solid 'dry ice' for cooling purposes and stage effects.

carbon monoxide: a colourless, odourless gas formed whenever carbon, or carbon-containing compounds, are burned in insufficient oxygen.

■ Carbon monoxide (CO) is highly toxic as it binds irreversibly to haemoglobin in the blood and prevents the transport of oxygen throughout the body. It can be emitted into a home from poorly maintained heating appliances and is present in inhaled tobacco smoke. In addition to the effects on adults, a reduced oxygen supply in a pregnant woman who smokes can affect a developing baby.

carboxylic acid: the general term given to the group of organic compounds that contain the $-CO_2H$ group.

■ Carboxylic acids are weak acids in solution. They can be formed industrially by the oxidation of *alcohols*.

■ *e.g.* The simplest carboxylic acid is methanoic acid (HCO_2H), which is given off by ants as a chemical defence. Ethanoic acid (CH_3CO_2H) in solution is commonly known as vinegar.

carcinogen: a substance that induces the development of a cancer.

■ Carcinogens damage cells so that they lose normal control over their activity. The damage may affect how often a cell reproduces or what products it makes.

The result is a clump of unusual cells, which can also spread to other parts of the body.

■ *e.g.* Cigarette smoke contains many carcinogens that induce lung cancer. Asbestos induces a different form of lung cancer.

cartilage: a stiff but flexible material found on the ends of bones and also used to support the ears and nose.

■ It gives the ends of bones a smooth, slippery surface so they move easily in joints. Sharks and related species have skeletons made entirely of cartilage.

catalyst: a substance that speeds up the rate of a chemical reaction, but that can be recovered unchanged at the end of the reaction.

■ Catalysts work by providing an alternative, lower-energy route by which a reaction can take place. If the catalyst is in the same state as the reactants it is known as homogeneous; if it is in a different state it is known as heterogeneous. Catalysts are used widely in industry.

■ *e.g.* Iron is used as a catalyst in the manufacture of ammonia; vanadium(v) oxide in the manufacture of sulphuric acid; and phosphoric(v) acid in the manufacture of ethanol from ethene.

cathode: the negative electrode in *electrolysis*.

cation: an atom or group of atoms that has lost one or more electrons.

■ Cations are formed during the process of ionic bonding.

■ *e.g.* Sodium ions (Na^+) and ammonium ions (NH_4^+).

cell, biological: the basic unit of all living things.

■ Some organisms exist as single cells. Many are multicellular, made up of many cells, with specialised cells carrying out particular functions.

■ *e.g.* Nerve cells, muscle cells, blood cells.

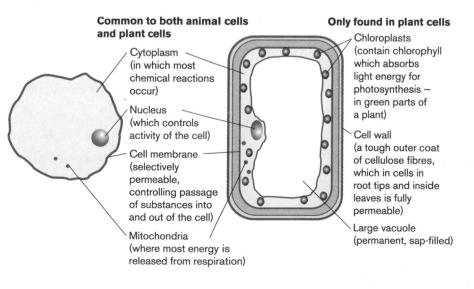

Common to both animal cells and plant cells

Cytoplasm (in which most chemical reactions occur)

Nucleus (which controls activity of the cell)

Cell membrane (selectively permeable, controlling passage of substances into and out of the cell)

Mitochondria (where most energy is released from respiration)

Only found in plant cells

Chloroplasts (contain chlorophyll which absorbs light energy for photosynthesis – in green parts of a plant)

Cell wall (a tough outer coat of cellulose fibres, which in cells in root tips and inside leaves is fully permeable)

Large vacuole (permanent, sap-filled)

C

As well as knowing what the different parts of cells do, you need to know which parts of cells are found in both animals and plants and which are found only in plants. And remember, a cell 'wall' is not like a brick wall — more like a tough string vest!

cell division: the process by which new cells are made. (See *mitosis, meiosis, binary fission.*)

cell, electrical: see *battery.*

cellulose: a *polymer* of glucose, making up a large part of plant cell walls.

cementation: the cementing together of small particles of sediment to form a *sedimentary rock.*
- The small particles of sediment are compacted together, squeezing out water from between the grains. Minerals such as silica and calcium carbonate are deposited between the grains and act as cement.
- *e.g.* Sandstone is a sedimentary rock in which the small sand grains have been cemented by silica or carbonate.

central nervous system: the parts of the nervous system involved in controlling and coordinating activity.
- The central nervous system is composed of the brain and spinal cord. The bones of the skull and spine protect it from physical damage.

centre of mass (also called 'centre of gravity'): the point at which all the mass of an object may be considered to be concentrated in working out the conditions for equilibrium.

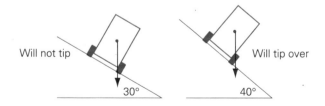

Will not tip / 30°   Will tip over / 40°

• = Centre of mass

- *e.g.* The position of the centre of mass of a vehicle will determine whether it will tip sideways on a slope.

centripetal force: the force needed to accelerate an object towards the centre when it is going round a circle.
- *e.g.* When whirling an object around on the end of a piece of string, you have to exert a centripetal force and keep pulling the object towards the centre of the circle.

C

The equal and opposite force to this (*Newton's third law*) is the outwards force that the object exerts on you. This is often called a 'centrifugal force', but you should avoid using this term which causes confusion; the motion can be explained satisfactorily without it. The apparent force that 'throws you sideways' when, for example, going round a corner in a car occurs because, as the car changes direction, it is accelerating round the corner but you are still tending to move at a steady speed in a straight line, for lack of a centripetal force.

CFC (chlorofluorocarbon): A substance once widely used as a propelling agent in aerosol cans, for cleaning grease from metal objects and as the cooling liquid in refrigerators.
■ In the stratosphere, CFCs break down and damage the ozone layer. Their use has now been banned in many but not all parts of the world.

chain reaction: a nuclear reaction in one atom that causes one or more reactions in other atoms.
■ In a nuclear reactor, *neutrons* from one uranium-235 atom are controlled so that they split just one further atom. In an atomic bomb they split more than one atom and there is an uncontrolled explosion.

chalk: a form of calcium carbonate ($CaCO_3$).
■ It is formed over millions of years when seashells and the skeletons of minute sea creatures are deposited on the floor of shallow seas. The shells are compacted to form sedimentary rock — chalk.

change of phase: see *change of state*.

change of state (also called 'change of phase')**:** a process that occurs when an element or compound goes from one physical state to another.
■ The change from a solid to a liquid is called melting (the reverse change is called solidifying or freezing); from a liquid to a gas it is called evaporating or boiling (the reverse is called condensing); and the change directly from a solid to a gas, without going through the liquid stage, is called sublimation.

charge: a quantity of electricity, symbol Q, measured in *coulombs*.
■ The charge flowing round a circuit equals the current in *amperes* (I) multiplied by the time in seconds (t). In *electrolysis* the charge is proportional to the *mass* of chemical liberated. In *electrostatics* charges may be positive or negative and are usually very small — about 10^{-8} coulomb.
■ *e.g.* $Q = I\,t$. If a current of 2 amps flows for 60 seconds a charge of 120 coulombs has passed round the circuit.

$Q = I\,t$ should be **QuIt**e easy to remember.

C

chemical formula: an arrangement of chemical symbols that shows which individual elements are combined in order to make a compound.

■ In an ionic compound (see *ionic bond*) the formula gives the ratios of the elements within the compound.

■ *e.g.* Sodium chloride (NaCl) has one sodium ion for every chloride ion.

■ For covalent compounds (see *covalent bond*) the formula gives the absolute number of atoms of each element within that compound.

■ *e.g.* A molecule of methane (CH_4) contains one carbon atom bonded to four hydrogen atoms.

chemical reaction: a reaction in which one or more new substances are made by reacting two or more substances together.

■ There is always a transfer of energy involved.

■ *e.g.* There are many different types of reaction such as decomposition, *redox*, *polymerisation* and precipitation.

chlor-alkali industry: a whole branch of industry based on the *electrolysis* of brine (concentrated sodium chloride solution).

■ In Britain, the brine is obtained from salt deposits in Cheshire. The industry consumes vast amounts of electricity.

■ *e.g.* Electrolysis of concentrated brine solutions gives chlorine (used for making polychloroethene, bleaches, pharmaceuticals and for treating water), sodium hydroxide solution (used for making soap, detergents, textiles and paper) and hydrogen (used for making nylon, margarine and as a fuel).

chlorine: a poisonous yellow-green gas.

■ It is found in group 7 of the periodic table (the halogens), and has seven electrons in its outermost electron shell. It is made by the *electrolysis* of brine in the *chlor-alkali industry*.

■ *e.g.* It is used for making polychloroethene, chlorinated solvents, paints, dyestuffs, weedkillers, pesticides and pharmaceuticals. It is also used to treat drinking water in order to kill any bacteria and make it fit to drink.

chlorophyll: a green pigment found in plants that traps light and makes the energy available for *photosynthesis*.

■ Chlorophyll is located in specialised *chloroplasts* in plant cells. The energy it harvests from light is used to convert carbon dioxide to glucose. Chlorophyll is best able to use red and blue wavelengths of light for photosynthesis.

chloroplast: a specialised structure responsible for *photosynthesis* in plant cells.

■ Parts of a plant above the ground are green because the cells contain chloroplasts, full of *chlorophyll,* which carry out photosynthesis. In the chloroplast, light energy is used to convert carbon dioxide to glucose. Palisade cells in the upper part of a leaf are specialised for photosynthesis by having large numbers of chloroplasts.

chromatid: one half of a *chromosome* as it appears during cell division.

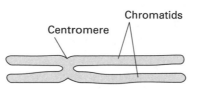

Centromere   Chromatids

■ Before a cell divides to make two new cells in *mitosis*, it makes a new copy of all its *DNA*. At the start of cell division, the DNA becomes visible as chromosomes. Each chromosome looks like two thick strands of material linked together at one point, called the centromere. Each of the thick strands is a chromatid and carries a set of genes that will be passed on to one or other of the new cells.

chromatography: the process of separating a mixture of compounds by allowing the mixture (dissolved in a suitable solvent) to move over a stationary phase (such as paper, alumina or inert gels).

■ The substances in the mixture travel at different speeds and eventually they are separated.

■ *e.g.* Absorbent paper is commonly used to separate out the colours in a mixture of dyes.

chromosome: a structure found in the nucleus of cells that carries inherited information in the form of *genes*.

■ Chromosomes are made of *DNA* coiled around proteins to make a stable structure. Each species of animal or plant has a typical number of chromosomes in the nuclei of their cells. Humans have 46, carried as 23 pairs. Chromosomes are duplicated before a cell divides to make new cells in *mitosis* and each daughter cell receives a complete set of chromosomes.

cilia: small hair-like extensions from the surface of a cell.

■ Cells carrying cilia are often found lining tubes and ducts in the body where they move fluids through the tubes.

■ *e.g.* The cells lining the trachea have cilia that move mucus out of the airways. They are damaged by cigarette smoke.

circuit breaker: a type of *relay* that switches off its own circuit when the current becomes excessive.

■ It can be reset when the fault has been removed and is often used instead of a *fuse*.

circuit, parallel: see *parallel circuit*.

circuit, series: see *series circuit*.

circulatory system: the organs and structures that are responsible for the

C

transportation of materials round the body.

■ The main components of the circulatory system are:

• blood, which transports materials

• arteries, veins and capillaries, which are blood vessels that convey blood to and from its destination

• the heart, which pumps the blood in one direction through blood vessels

classification: arranging living things into sets according to the number of features they have in common.

■ The classification groups are based on important features, such as the pattern of the skeleton, method of reproduction and internal body structures. Groups with many important features in common are thought to have evolved from a common ancestor.

■ *e.g.* All vertebrates have a brain at the head end, four limbs, a spinal column and a post-anal tail.

clone: a group of genetically identical individuals.

■ Many organisms use *asexual reproduction* which results in a cluster of offspring that are genetically identical to their parent, and form a clone. Identical twins could also be described as a clone as they are genetically identical.

■ A clone can also be derived from a single parent using *biotechnology*. Taking cuttings is a form of plant cloning but *micropropagation* techniques generate thousands more plants from a small sample of cells from a single plant. This produces large numbers of genetically identical plantlets. Animals are far more difficult to clone. Scientists have succeeded in using nuclei from an adult's cells to replace the nuclei in fertilised eggs and have raised young that are genetically identical to the nucleus-donating parent. Gene cloning is the process of transferring a gene into suitable bacteria which will then duplicate many copies of the gene.

closed: the state of *switch* or *relay* contacts when they are joined. See also *open*.

coal: a solid black material with a high carbon content formed over millions of years from the remains of vegetation from swamps.

■ Vegetation dies and falls to the bottom of swamps. Due to the anaerobic conditions the material does not rot, turning the vegetation firstly into peat. If this is buried by other deposits, heat and pressure from the overlying material turns this peat into coal. Different types of coal may be formed depending on the degree of compaction and heat involved.

coke: coal that has been heated strongly in a lack of air. Volatile organic substances are removed and a porous form of carbon remains.

■ It is widely used in the smelting of metals.

collision: a meeting of one or more moving *masses*.

■ In any collision with no external forces acting, the total momentum of the colliding masses is conserved *(conservation of momentum)*. However, energy will be lost unless the collision is perfectly elastic. A collision might not involve actual contact, for example when two like magnetic poles meet and repel each other. In the *Rutherford model of the atom*, positive alpha particles are repelled by positive nuclei without touching them.

combustion (also called 'burning'): the term given to the *oxidation* process whereby substances combine with oxygen, usually from the air.
■ Heat and light are evolved and the process is always *exothermic*.
■ *e.g.* Organic compounds always produce carbon dioxide and water if they are combusted in an excess of oxygen.

comet: a small body in the *solar system* whose orbit around the Sun is a very flat *ellipse*.
■ Comets are visible for periods of only a few weeks but reappear after many years.

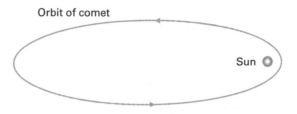
Orbit of comet

Sun

communications satellite: a *satellite* in a synchronous orbit around the Earth.
■ The satellite orbits the Earth once a day moving in the same direction as the Earth, and so remains above a fixed point on the equator. It receives and re-transmits radio, television, telephone and data signals between ground stations.

commutator: the copper connections on the *armature* of a d.c. *motor* or *generator* which are connected to the rotating coils and allow the current to change direction in the coils. See also *brush*.

compound: a substance made up of two or more elements chemically bonded together.
■ *e.g.* Sulphuric acid (H_2SO_4) and sodium chloride (NaCl) are examples of compounds.

concentration: a measure of the amount of a substance — usually in a given volume of solvent.
■ Concentrations are commonly expressed in moles of substance dissolved in 1 cubic decimetre (dm^3) of solvent (water).
■ *e.g.* A solution of sodium chloride (molecular mass 58.5) containing 5.85 g of solid in 1 dm^3 of water has a concentration of 0.1 mol/dm^3.

TIP
Concentration — particularly of an acid — should not be confused with its strength (the number of H^+ ions the acid puts into solution).

C

condensation reaction: a reaction in which two molecules (usually organic) combine to form another molecule and also a molecule of water.

■ In organic chemistry any reaction that gives off a small molecule as a by-product (HCl, CH_3OH, etc.) may be called a condensation reaction.

■ *e.g.* The esterification of ethanol with ethanoic acid to form ethyl ethanoate and water.

condenser: a glass tube over which cold water passes. Gases pass through the tube, are cooled, and condense back into a liquid.

■ A condenser is used in the process of *distillation* to condense the vapours of a liquid that has been boiled off.

conditioned reflex: a piece of learned behaviour that occurs in response to a specific *stimulus*.

■ The Russian physiologist Pavlov observed that dogs salivated when their handler approached with their food; they had associated a sight with something they wanted. Pavlov trained dogs to associate the sound of a bell (a stimulus) with the appearance of their food (a reward). After a few experiences the dogs began to salivate (the behaviour response) as soon as they heard the bell, even if there was no food.

■ *e.g.* This technique is used for training, for example teaching a dog to sit up and beg. The conditioned behaviour is lost if the reward is not given at least some of the time.

conduction, heat: the process by which heat travels through a solid.

■ As 'hot' atoms vibrate, their energy is passed on to neighbouring atoms which become hot. The free *electrons* in a metal also help to pass on heat and so metals are good conductors of heat as well as of electricity.

conductor, electrical: graphite, an *electrolyte* or any metal that has a low *resistance* to the flow of electricity.

■ In solid conductors, *electrons* move freely from one atom to another. In liquids and gases, positive and negative *ions* conduct the electricity.

■ *e.g.* Copper is one of the best conductors of electricity and is used in most cables.

conductor, heat: any substance, usually a metal, that conducts *heat* well from one place to another.

■ Metals that are good electrical conductors are also good heat conductors.

■ *e.g.* Saucepans made of stainless steel, which is not a very good conductor, often have a thick layer of copper, a good conductor, in the base.

conglomerate: a sedimentary rock made by the cementation of small pebbles and rocks.

■ Rock fragments bigger than 2mm are carried downstream by rivers. The rocks become compacted and as the water is squeezed out, silica and carbonates are deposited, cementing the particles together.

conservation of energy: the theory that *energy* can neither be created nor destroyed but can only be transformed from one form to another.
■ However, in nuclear reactions small amounts of mass can be transformed into large amounts of energy.

conservation of momentum: in any event, such as a collision, where no external forces are acting, the total *momentum* before the collision is equal to the total momentum after the collision.

TIP
Remember that momentum has direction as well as magnitude and, if momentum in one direction is taken as positive, momentum in the opposite direction must be taken as negative.

constellation: a group of *stars* or *nebulae*, sometimes having a popular name.
■ *e.g.* Andromeda is a nebula in the constellation of Orion.

consumer: an organism that obtains its energy by eating another organism.
■ Plants produce food as a result of photosynthesis. Animals that eat plants for food are primary consumers. Predators that obtain their food by eating animals that eat vegetation are secondary consumers.

contact process: the process for the manufacture of sulphuric acid.
■ Sulphur is burnt in air to form sulphur dioxide. The sulphur dioxide is mixed with more oxygen and is oxidised to sulphur trioxide in the presence of a vanadium(v) oxide *catalyst*. This is then dissolved in concentrated sulphuric acid to make slightly more concentrated acid. The acid can be diluted to the required concentration. Care is taken to prevent the emission of sulphur dioxide or trioxide into the atmosphere as these can both cause *acid rain*.

continental drift: the movement of the Earth's tectonic plates about its surface.
■ Plates generally move at a rate of a few centimetres a year — approximately the speed at which your fingernails grow. Over the course of time continental drift has changed the face of the Earth, breaking up one giant continent (Pangaea) and moving the pieces of the continent to the positions they now occupy.

contraception: techniques aimed at preventing pregnancy by reducing the chances of a sperm fertilising an egg.
■ Barrier methods use physical intervention such as a condom or diaphragm to prevent sperm passing along the reproductive tract and reaching an egg. A spermicide may be used at the same time to kill the sperm. Hormonal methods, such as the pill, mimic the hormone changes in a pregnant woman's body to stop a new egg developing. (See *menstrual cycle*.)

convection: the process by which *heat* is transferred by the movement of warm liquid or gas.

C

■ In natural convection, warm air (which is less dense than cold air) rises, transferring heat. It is replaced by colder air. The same process is used in many hot-water systems. In forced convection, a pump can force warm liquid or a fan can blow hot air in any direction.

■ *e.g.* Central heating systems used to rely on natural convection but now they usually have pumps that force hot water upwards, downwards or sideways towards the radiators.

copper: a red-brown metal found within the transition metals group of the periodic table.

■ Copper is extracted from its ores (usually the sulphide) by *reduction* and then purified by *electrolysis*. It is a good conductor of heat and electricity and exhibits *malleability* and *ductility*. It is used for wiring and in cooking utensils. It is often alloyed with other elements, for example in brass and bronze. (See *conductor, heat* and *conductor, electrical.*)

core: the dense, central part of the Earth.

■ It consists of two parts — the inner core, which is solid, and the outer core, which is liquid. It has a density about 10 times that of water, a diameter of about 3500 km and is composed mainly of nickel and iron. The core of the Earth is at a temperature of about 7600°C.

corrosion: the chemical breakdown of a metal surface by gases or liquids.

■ In order to prevent corrosion occurring, metal surfaces are often covered with a layer of paint, grease, plastic or with another metal such as chromium.

■ *e.g.* Water and oxygen commonly attack iron, forming *rust*.

cosmic radiation (also called 'cosmic rays'): highly penetrating particles such as *protons* and helium atoms which reach the Earth from space. Those of low energy come from the Sun and those of high energy from our *galaxy* and beyond — possibly from *supernovae*.

cosmic rays: see *cosmic radiation.*

coulomb: the unit of electrical *charge,* symbol *C*.

■ 1 coulomb flows round a circuit when a current of 1 amp flows for 1 second. The charge on 6.24×10^{18} electrons is a negative charge of 1 coulomb.

covalent bond: a bond formed between two non-metallic elements when the atoms share electrons in order to attain a full, stable, outer shell of electrons.

■ The bond is localised between the atoms concerned — it is directional.

cracking: the industrial process whereby long-chained hydrocarbons are passed over a *catalyst* at high temperatures and pressures for a short period of time. The long chain breaks down, producing a mixture of short-chain *alkanes* and *alkenes*.

■ Cracking is an important part of the petrochemical industry as shorter chained hydrocarbons are more in demand than long-chain hydrocarbons.

crop rotation: an agricultural practice of cultivating a piece of land with different crops in sequence, over a period of several years.
- It stops pest numbers building up and replenishes some nutrients removed by particular crops. Clover or other nitrogen-fixing plants are included in the rotation to increase the nitrate content of soils.

crude oil (also called 'petroleum'): a natural mineral oil found underground in permeable rocks.
- This thick, brown, flammable liquid consists of hydrocarbons mixed with other elements in varying proportions. It is derived from ancient organic material that has been converted into oil by bacterial action, heat and pressure. From crude oil, various products are made by distillation and other processes. Examples include fuel oil, petrol, kerosene, diesel and lubricating oil. Crude oil products are used in large quantities for the manufacture of detergents, fibres, plastics, pesticides, fertilisers and pharmaceuticals.

crust: the outermost layer of the Earth's surface.
- It varies from 8 to 65 km thick. Continental crust carries the continents and is less dense than the oceanic crust. The Earth's crust is divided into several plates which slowly move about the surface due to convection currents deep within the body of the Earth.

cryolite: the mineral sodium aluminium fluoride (Na_3AlF_6).
- It is added to *bauxite* during the manufacture of aluminium by *electrolysis*, in order to reduce the melting point of the ore. Most cryolite used nowadays is manufactured.

crystal: a regularly shaped solid that consists of particles in a lattice.
- Crystals are formed by the slow cooling of saturated solutions, or of molten liquids. Crystals of the same substance are always of the same shape.

current: a flow of electric *charge* measured in *amperes*, symbol I.
- 1 amp is a charge of 1 *coulomb* flowing every second. Current in amps = charge in coulombs/time in seconds:

$$I = Q/t$$

The current is the same at all points of a *series circuit*. At a junction the current divides, but the sum of the currents arriving at the junction equals the sum of the currents leaving it. The current can be measured by an *ammeter* connected in series.

TIP

In a circuit, *electrons* flow from the negative terminal of the power supply to the positive, but conventional current is taken to flow from positive to negative. In *electrolyte*, positive *ions* flow from positive to negative and negative ions flow from negative to positive.

C

cystic fibrosis: an inherited condition that affects lungs and the digestive system.
■ The condition is carried by a recessive *allele*. Individuals who inherit two copies of the allele for cystic fibrosis, one from each parent, develop the condition. The allele's effects lead to the production of thick, sticky mucus in the lungs, the pancreatic duct and other places. People who carry one normal allele and one cystic fibrosis allele are not affected.

Darwinian theory: the mechanism of *evolution* by *natural selection* proposed by Charles Darwin.

d.c.: see *direct current.*

d.c. generator: a rotating machine that converts mechanical energy into electrical energy in the form of a *direct current.*
■ The machine has one or more coils rotating in a magnetic field and connected to a *commutator.* Fixed *brushes* pass the current to a circuit. The magnetic field may be provided by fixed permanent *magnets* in a small machine or by fixed coils carrying a direct current in a large machine.

decay, radioactive: the process by which a radioactive element becomes weaker as the atoms emit radiation and change into another element. (See *half-life, carbon dating.*)

decomposer: an organism that uses dead plant or animal material as a food source.
■ Decomposers include fungi, beetles, earthworms, minute soil invertebrates and bacteria. Larger decomposers, or detritivores, eat or bite large pieces of material and reduce it to fragments of detritus. Fungi and bacteria secrete *enzymes* that break down fragments and release nutrients. Gradually, large molecules such as cellulose and protein are degraded into smaller molecules.

deficiency disease: a disorder in plants or animals resulting from the lack of a specific nutrient.
■ Deficiency diseases usually refer to problems caused by a lack of a vitamin or mineral. These nutrients are usually needed in small quantities in the diet.
■ *e.g.* Iron deficiency in humans can result in too few red blood cells, giving rise to the condition called anaemia. Magnesium deficiency in plants leads to yellowing leaves, due to a lack of *chlorophyll.*

deforestation: the removal of forest and woodland from an area.
■ This causes major ecological problems. There is a loss of habitat for forest animal

and plant species. The local populations decline or disappear altogether and this affects local food webs. The loss of trees reduces the amount of humus entering the soil and allows the ground to dry out. The soil becomes impoverished. Deforested areas in mountainous regions no longer absorb heavy rain and flooding and erosion may occur.

dehydration: the removal of water from a compound.
■ Dehydration can occur through physical processes (e.g. heating) or by chemical means.
■ *e.g.* If concentrated sulphuric acid is added to sugar (a carbohydrate), water is removed and only carbon remains.

denatured: a denatured protein molecule has had its shape altered so that it does its job less well.
■ Changes in pH and heat above a critical temperature cause proteins to coagulate. This is important for *enzymes* because the shape change will alter the part (called the *active site*) that catalyses a chemical reaction.
■ *e.g.* This happens when fluid, transparent, raw egg-white is fried. As it denatures it coagulates into a white solid.

dendrite: one of many small branching extensions of the cell body of a *neurone*.
■ Dendrites receive impulses from other neurones, which are then channelled out along the *axon*.

denitrification: a process in which soil microorganisms use nitrate ions and release *nitrogen* gas.
■ This is the part of the *nitrogen cycle* that returns nitrogen to the atmosphere. Bacteria in the soil release nitrate ions from dead animal and plant material, which are taken up by plants. Nitrate-reducing bacteria, which thrive in waterlogged soils, use the nitrate and reduce the amount available for plant growth.

density: the *mass* of a substance divided by its volume, measured in kg/m^3 or g/cm^3.
■ The more dense a substance is, the 'heavier' it feels. Dense solids or liquids sink in less dense liquids. A substance in gaseous form (e.g. steam) is normally much less dense than in liquid form (e.g. water) because the molecules are much further apart.
■ *e.g.* The density of a block of aluminium measuring $5\,cm \times 4\,cm \times 3\,cm$ with a mass of $162\,g$ is $162\,g/(5 \times 4 \times 3)\,cm^3 = 162/60\,g/cm^3 = 2.7\,g/cm^3$.

TIP   The density of water is $1\,g/cm^3$ (and also $1000\,kg/m^3$) at $4°C$.

deposition: the depositing of small particles of rock and other material that have been carried along by streams and rivers.
■ This will usually occur in river deltas and estuaries. The deposition of particles over a long period of time eventually results in the formation of *sedimentary rock*.

d

desalination: the removal of salt from brackish water to make it fit to drink.
■ Heat is used to evaporate the water. It is then condensed as pure water. The process is energy-intensive and normally only used where energy is plentiful and cheap.

detergent: a cleaning agent made from the reaction of hydrocarbons with sulphuric acid.
■ It is unaffected by hard water (which can prevent soap from working effectively). The detergent molecule consists of a charged 'head' and a neutral 'tail'. The hydrocarbon tail is attracted to dirt or grease, while the charged head repels other detergent molecules and so lifts the dirt from the fabric being cleaned.

diabetes: a medical condition in which an individual has problems regulating the amount of glucose in the blood.
■ Blood glucose concentrations are controlled by insulin from the pancreas. Insulin is released when the blood concentration rises. It causes cells in the liver and muscles to take in glucose and store it as *glycogen*. Diabetes occurs when the pancreas makes too little insulin. High concentrations of blood glucose have harmful effects on the tissues — little is stored and some is lost in urine. Another form of diabetes is due to cells failing to respond to insulin.

dialysis: the artificial filtering of blood by passing it over a partially permeable membrane.
■ A dialysis fluid runs along the other side of the partially permeable membrane. It contains dissolved materials in carefully calculated amounts. Unwanted dissolved substances diffuse out of the blood through the membrane into the fluid on the other side, along a concentration gradient, and are removed.

diamond: an *allotrope* of carbon.
■ It consists of a regular array of carbon atoms bonded to each other in a three-dimensional network. Each carbon atom is bonded to four others. Diamond is transparent and does not conduct electricity. It is the hardest naturally occurring substance known.

d

■ *e.g.* Diamonds are used for jewellery and on the tips of drilling and cutting instruments.

differentiation: the changes a cell undergoes after it has been produced by cell division in order to adapt it for a particular function.

■ *e.g.* Red blood cells are produced in bone marrow. Initially they are like most other cells but they synthesise a huge amount of haemoglobin, lose their nucleus, and develop a characteristic shape. These features adapt them to carry oxygen.

diffraction: the process by which *waves* going though a gap or around a small obstacle spread out sideways from the edges of the gap.

■ The amount of diffraction depends on the wavelength and on the width of the slit; the diffraction is greater for long waves and for narrow gaps. Long waves going past small obstacles tend to join up after passing the obstacle.

■ *e.g.* You can see diffraction of light by looking at a small point of light such as a distant street light or a torch bulb (without a reflector). Hold two pieces of card with straight edges close to your eye. As you bring the pieces of card very close together the light will appear to spread out.

diffusion: the movement of small particles from a region of high concentration to an area of low concentration.

■ Diffusion occurs fastest in gases and slowest in solutions. Diffusion in solids is negligible.

digestion: the process of breaking down large, insoluble molecules in food to smaller, soluble molecules that can pass through the gut wall into the blood.

■ Nutrients such as starch and proteins are large molecules that cannot diffuse through the cells lining the gut to enter the bloodstream. Enzymes break them down into smaller subunits of glucose and amino acids, respectively, which can diffuse through into the bloodstream.

digital: a method of representing or transmitting information in steps or by on–off voltages, rather than by continuous variation.

■ *e.g.* It can apply to various technologies:
  - a digital voltmeter might show a voltage of 3.4 V or 3.5 V but cannot show any value in between these.
  - digital electronic circuits have outputs that are on or off but cannot be 'half on'.
  - digital telephone and radio transmissions sample the voltage output of a microphone about 40 000 times a second and each time the voltage is converted into a series of on–off pulses. At the receiver these pulses are converted back into a sound wave. Digital television works in a similar way. Both techniques enable far more information to be transmitted than would be possible with *analogue* techniques.

d

This simplified diagram shows how an analogue wave (the curve) can be sampled and turned into a series of on–off signals (ones and noughts) for digital transmission.

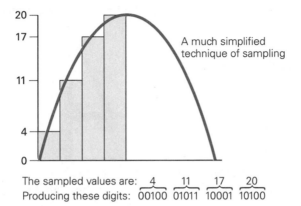

A much simplified technique of sampling

The sampled values are: 4   11   17   20
Producing these digits: 00100 01011 10001 10100

dilution: the process of reducing the *concentration* of a solution — usually by the addition of more solvent.

TIP
When an acid is diluted, the acid is added to water. In this way the dilution is performed safely as any heat generated by the dilution is dispersed throughout the solution.

diode: an electrical component that allows *current* in a *series circuit* to flow in one direction but not in the opposite direction.

■ **e.g.** A diode in series with a lamp will turn *alternating current* into *direct current*.

TIP
Conventional current can flow through the diode in the direction of the arrow that is part of the circuit symbol. When this current flows, the *potential difference* across the diode is about 0.5 V for all currents up to the maximum permitted. The diode cannot be said to have a particular *resistance*.

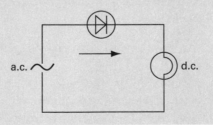

a.c.   d.c.

direct current (d.c.): a current that flows in one direction only.

■ It is usually produced by *batteries, d.c. generators* and *solar cells*. If it is produced from a.c. using a *diode*, the current fluctuates, but flows only in one direction. Smoothing circuits are usually added after the diode to produce a steady current.

d

displacement: a reaction that occurs when one element displaces another from a solution of its compounds.
■ *e.g.* A metal high in the reactivity series will displace a metal lower in the series from a solution of its ions. Similarly, a more reactive halogen will displace a less reactive halogen from a solution of its ions:
$$Cl_2 + 2I^- \longrightarrow 2Cl^- + I_2$$

dissociation: the reversible breakdown of a molecule or ion into smaller parts.
■ *e.g.* Water dissociates into ions:
$$H_2O \rightleftharpoons H^+ + OH^-$$
and ammonia can dissociate into its constituent gases:
$$2NH_3 \rightleftharpoons N_2 + 3H_2$$

dissolution (also called 'dissolving'): the process whereby a solid or liquid is dispersed into solution in such small particles that they can no longer be seen by the the naked eye.
■ The substance that has dissolved is spread evenly throughout the solution.

dissolving: see *dissolution*.

distance/time graph: a graph of the distance travelled by an object, plotted vertically, against time, plotted horizontally.
■ The gradient (slope) of the graph gives the speed of the object.

TIP If the graph is horizontal, the object is not moving.

distillation: the process of separating mixtures (either of solids in liquids, or of liquids with different boiling points) by boiling off the more volatile liquid and condensing it.
■ The liquid that condenses is called the distillate. For mixtures of liquids with close boiling points, fractional distillation is used. The vapours pass into a column where they can condense and distil many times — each time becoming richer in the more volatile liquid.

DNA: deoxyribonucleic acid—a *nucleic acid* that encodes genetic information in cells.
■ DNA is found in chromosomes in the nucleus of cells. It is a huge polymer composed of twin strands made of repeating sugar (deoxyribose) and phosphate subunits, linked together by *bases*. The molecule is twisted into a double helix shape, which in turn is coiled around protein molecules for stability. Four types of base are used in the molecule: adenine (A), thymine (T), cytosine (C) and guanine (G). The sequence of bases along one strand of the molecule encodes genetic information. The information is divided up into lengths called *genes* which encode how to assemble a single protein. Within the gene the bases are read in groups of three to determine the structure of the protein.

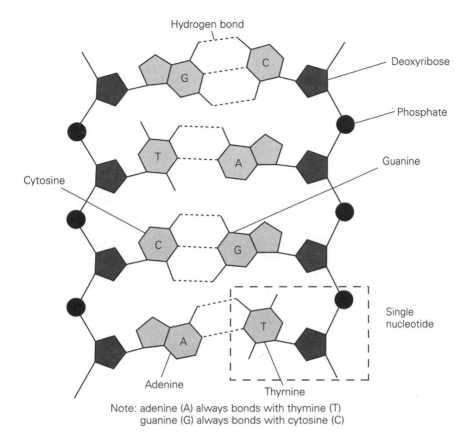

Note: adenine (A) always bonds with thymine (T)
guanine (G) always bonds with cytosine (C)

dominant allele: an *allele* that is expressed if it is present in the chromosomes.
■ Chromosomes carry a pair of alleles for genetic features. If one of these is a dominant form, that version will function even if the alternative *recessive allele* is also present.

Doppler effect: the effect that makes the *frequency* of a *wave* received by an observer higher or lower than the wave emitted by a moving source.
■ The frequency is higher if the source is moving towards the observer and lower if the source is moving away. Similar effects are noticed if the observer is moving towards or away from the source of waves.
■ *e.g.* The sound you hear from a vehicle that is moving towards you will have a higher frequency than the sound actually emitted, and a lower frequency as it moves away. The effect is also seen as a *red shift* in the light from stars that are receding from us. A star must be moving much faster than a vehicle for this effect to be noticed as the speed of light is about 1 million times greater than the speed of sound.

double bond: a bond formed when two elements joined by *covalent bonds* share two electrons from each atom.

d

■When the double bond is formed between carbon atoms the molecule containing the bond is said to be unsaturated (see *unsaturated compound*). Carbon–carbon double bonds are highly reactive.

double circulation: the movement of blood through two separate loops of the circulatory system, and hence through the heart twice, during one circuit of the body.

■One loop serves the lungs and the other serves the rest of the body. Blood leaving the left side of the heart is carried to all other organs where it exchanges materials with the cells. It returns to the right side of the heart to be pumped into the blood vessels serving the lungs. In the lungs it gains oxygen and loses carbon dioxide. It returns to the left side of the heart to be pumped to the rest of the body again.

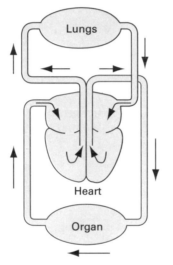

double helix: the shape of a *DNA* molecule.

■The two chains of sugar–phosphate subunits make right-handed spirals around each other. Bonds between the bases attached to each chain link the two chains together at regular intervals.

double insulation: two levels of insulation used in electrical equipment that does not need an earth wire (see *earth, electrical*).

■Such equipment has no exposed metal that might become live if there were a fault and carries the symbol ▣. There is no green and yellow wire and no earth connection in the *plug*.

drug: a substance that alters the activity of cells and organs within the individual taking it.

■Drugs are classified according to the type of chemical they contain, by the disease or disorder they are used to treat or by their effects on our bodies. Some drugs fall into more than one category.

■ *e.g.* Antibiotics are clinical drugs used to kill infecting microrganisms. Solvents affect behaviour and damage lungs, liver and brain. Alcohol affects the function of the brain and can damage it and the liver. Tobacco smoke contains nicotine which causes addiction, substances such as tar which can cause lung diseases, including cancer, and substances that cause damage to the circulatory system. *Carbon monoxide* in smoke also causes harm. Caffeine, found in coffee, tea and cola, is used for its stimulating effect. Heroin is a highly addictive drug that forces users into a major change of lifestyle in order to supply the addiction.

dry ice: the common name for solid carbon dioxide.

■ This undergoes *sublimation* at −78°C and so is used as a refrigerant. It is also used to make the familiar low-lying fog in stage productions.

dry mass: the mass of plant or animal material after water has been removed by drying it out in an oven.

■ The water content of living tissue varies according to an organism's most recent experiences, and can vary significantly without there being any more or less cellular material present. Using dry mass allows materials of differing water content to be compared.

■ *e.g.* A limp lettuce can gain 20% more mass if it is left for a period in a bowl of water and yet will not have made any new material.

ductility: the ability of a substance to be pulled into a wire.

■ *e.g.* Most metals are ductile, a good example being copper.

dynamo: an electromagnetic machine that converts mechanical energy into a.c. or d.c. electrical supply. (See *a.c. generator, d.c. generator.*)

earth, electrical: a conducting connection that joins an appliance to the earth.

■ Any electrical appliance with exposed metal parts should have its metal connected to the earth so that if a fault develops, the *fuse* will blow and it will be safe to touch the metal. In a 13-amp *plug* the earth connection goes to the largest pin via a cable with green and yellow insulation. An earth connection is not needed with equipment that has *double insulation.*

earthquake: a shaking of the Earth that occurs when stresses within it are released suddenly.

■ Earthquakes produce *P waves* and *S waves*. These waves create vibrations that can cause severe damage to property. They usually occur at plate boundaries. The strength of an earthquake is measured on the Richter scale — an increment of one unit on the scale means an earthquake 10 times more violent.

echo: a reflection of a *sound wave* from a hard object.

■ Echoes of sound waves can be used to measure the speed of sound and also to locate objects submerged in water. Echoes of *ultrasonic waves* are used to measure distances of several metres. See *ultrasonic ranging.*

■ *e.g.* An echo of a bang is reflected from a wall 82 metres away and heard after 0.5 seconds. The sound has travelled 164 metres in 0.5 seconds and so the speed of sound is 164 m/0.5 s = 328 m/s.

TIP Don't forget that the sound has to travel to the wall *and* back.

ecosystem: an ecological term that describes a network of living organisms interacting with an environment that is defined by one or two key factors.

■ Ecosystems are often defined by physical factors such as the persistent low temperature of the Antarctic ecosystem, or low water availability of a desert ecosystem, or high temperature and humidity of a rainforest ecosystem. The energy flow is largely contained within the ecosystem, with little input from other ecosystems. An ecosystem encompasses a number of different *habitats*, which may be comparable with similar habitats in a different ecosystem.

effector: a structure that responds to a nervous impulse.
- In a *reflex* arc the effector is often a muscle, but it can also be a gland.
- *e.g.* In the pupil reflex a high light intensity results in an effector — the circular muscles of the iris — contracting to reduce the diameter of the pupil and reduce the amount of light entering the eye. The smell of a lemon causes a flow of saliva from the salivary glands.

effervescence: bubbling due to gas release from a substance in solution.
- *e.g.* When a carbonate is added to acid, bubbles of carbon dioxide are given off — the solution effervesces.

efficiency: the useful *work done* divided by the total *energy* used. It is usually expressed as a percentage.
- *e.g.* An electric motor uses 80 joules of electrical energy to raise a weight of 10 newtons through a height of 4 metres. The efficiency is 10×4 joules/80 joules $= 0.5 = 50\%$.

TIP
Efficiency has no units as it is a ratio of energy/energy.

elastic limit: the furthest that an elastic material will stretch and still return to its original size when it is released.
- If it is stretched beyond the elastic limit it will acquire a permanent stretch and might break.

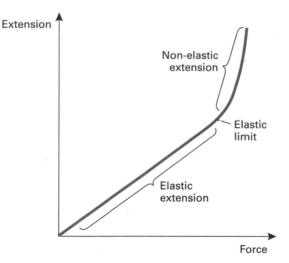

elastic potential energy: *energy* stored in a spring or any elastic material when it is stretched or compressed.
- Most of this energy is recovered when the spring is released.
- *e.g.* When an elastic ball bounces it has maximum deformation when it is stationary for an instant. The elastic potential energy stored is changed into *kinetic energy* as the ball rises again.

e

electrical cell: see *battery*.

electrical energy: the energy transferred from an *electromotive force* along cables to an appliance which then transforms the electrical energy into some other form.

▪ *e.g.* The *kinetic energy* needed to drive an *a.c. generator* in a power station is transferred to electrical energy which is carried along wires to a house. Here it might drive a *motor* of a vacuum cleaner which transfers the electrical energy to kinetic energy of the moving air.

electricity meter: a meter that measures the amount of electrical energy used in *joules* or *kilowatt hours.*

▪ The domestic electric meter multiplies the current by the voltage by the time and the result is used to calculate the cost of all the electrical energy supplied to a house.

▪ *e.g.* A 230 V lamp takes 0.5 A and is switched on for 10 hours. The energy used is $230 \times 0.5 \times 10 = 1150$ watt hours = 1.15 kW hours = 1.15 units.

TIP

The cost of electricity = the price per unit × the number of units used.

electrochemical series: a list of elements arranged in order of their ability to donate electrons to their *ions* in solution.

▪ The further apart two elements are in the series the more reactive they are towards one another.

▪ *e.g.* Potassium is high in the electrochemical series; chlorine is low in the series.

electrode: a conductor that will take in or give out electrons when part of an electrochemical cell.

▪ Electrodes are usually made of metal or graphite.

electrolysis: the decomposition of a substance by the passage of electricity.

▪ Electricity enters the solution (the *electrolyte*) through *electrodes*. The electrolyte might be decomposed (for example molten sodium chloride produces sodium at the cathode and chlorine at the anode) or the electrodes might react (for example in the purification of copper the anode dissolves into solution).

electrolyte: the solution that is decomposed during the process of electrolysis.

▪ *e.g.* The electrolyte can be either an ionic substance dissolved in water or a molten ionic substance, such as alumina in the manufacture of aluminium.

electromagnet: a magnet made of a coil of wire carrying a *direct current.*

▪ The strength of the magnet is proportional to the number of turns in the coil and to the size of the current. The strength of the magnet is greater if it has a soft iron core and very much greater if there is a complete iron circuit with no air gap.

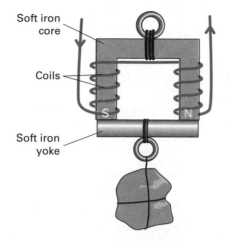

Soft iron
core

Coils

Soft iron
yoke

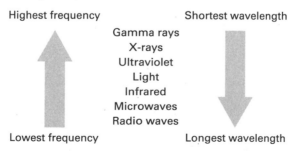

electromagnetic induction: the production of an *electromotive force (e.m.f.)* by moving a magnet past a conductor, or a conductor past a magnet, or by changing the strength of magnetism passing through a coil of wire.

■ The size of the e.m.f. is proportional to the rate of movement or to the rate at which the magnetism changes, and to the number of turns in the coil. If the conductor is part of a complete circuit the e.m.f. will drive a current; this is called an induced current.

■ *e.g.* In a *d.c. generator* a coil rotates in a magnetic field; in an *a.c. generator* a magnet rotates inside a coil. In a *transformer* nothing moves, but the *alternating current* in the primary coil causes changing magnetism in the iron core and this induces an e.m.f. in the secondary coil.

electromagnetic spectrum: all the *electromagnetic waves* that transfer energy by radiation.

■ The spectrum comprises, in order of increasing frequency and decreasing wavelength: radio waves, microwaves, infrared, visible light, ultraviolet, X-rays and gamma rays.

Highest frequency   Shortest wavelength

Gamma rays
X-rays
Ultraviolet
Light
Infrared
Microwaves
Radio waves

Lowest frequency   Longest wavelength

electromagnetic wave: a wave that needs no material substance for its propagation and travels through space at a speed of 3×10^8 m/s.

■ Electromagnetic waves include all the waves of the *electromagnetic spectrum*

e

from radio waves (about 100 kHz) to *gamma rays* (about 10^{23} Hz). As their name suggests, these waves are transmitted by oscillations of electric and magnetic fields.

electromotive force (e.m.f.): the electrical force that can drive a *current* round a circuit, measured in volts (V) and often called a *voltage*.
■ It is normally produced by a *battery*, a *d.c. generator*, an *a.c. generator*, a *solar cell* or a fuel cell. There is an e.m.f. whenever some other form of energy is being transformed into electrical energy.

electron: one of the three fundamental particles that make up atoms.
■ Electrons have a negligible mass and are negatively charged. They circulate around a central nucleus of protons and neutrons. The electrons are arranged in shells around the nucleus. The first (inner) shell holds a maximum of two electrons; the second shell contains a maximum of eight electrons. The number of electrons in the outermost shell (i.e. those that are involved in bonding) is the same as the group number of that element in the periodic table.
■ *e.g.* Sodium (group 1) has one electron in its outermost shell.

electroplating: the deposition of one metal on another using *electrolysis*.
■ The object to be plated is made the cathode, and a solution of a compound of the metal to be deposited is used as the electrolyte. Generally, objects are electroplated to increase their resistance to corrosion.
■ *e.g.* Steel bicycle handlebars are often chromium plated.

electrostatics: the study of stationary electric *charges*.
■ Stationary charges are usually very small (about 10^{-8} coulomb) and voltages high (about 2000 V). This means that insulation needs to be extremely good to prevent charges leaking away.
■ *e.g.* In dry conditions, charges produced by friction can give rise to high enough voltages to produce sparks which can start fires or explosions.

TIP

Charges can be produced by rubbing an insulator, such as a plastic ruler, with a dry cloth. If this should rub electrons off the plastic ruler, they will remain in the region, attracted by the positive charge on the ruler, until they can return to the ruler and discharge it. As the duster is not a very good insulator, the electrons can move through it and through the person's body, staying near to the ruler. They will not disappear.

Plastic ruler

Duster

element: a substance that is made up of atoms of the same *atomic number*.
■ Each element has a different number of protons. (See *periodic table*.)

elementary particle: there are three elementary particles: *protons, neutrons* and *electrons*, which in combination make up atoms.
■ Protons have a relative mass of 1 and a positive charge. Neutrons also have a relative mass of 1 but no charge. Electrons have a relative mass of 1/1836 and a negative charge. Protons and neutrons are found within the central nucleus of an atom, with the electrons circulating around in shells.

ellipse: the shape formed by the path of a *planet, satellite* or any other object in orbit around a more massive object, under the influence of *gravity*.
■ The orbits of the planets, except Mercury and Pluto, are very close to circles, but *comets* have very elongated elliptical orbits.

TIP
An ellipse is like a 'squashed circle'. You can draw one by putting a loop of string loosely around two pins and tracing around the pins using a pencil placed inside the loop, keeping it taut.

embryo: the structure produced by repeated cell divisions (*mitosis*) after fertilisation.
■ In humans an embryo becomes a fetus at about 7 weeks, when the first bone cells appear.

e.m.f.: see *electromotive force*.

empirical formula: the simplest ratio in which atoms combine in a given substance.
■ It does not have to be the same as the formula of the molecule.
■ *e.g.* The empirical formula of butene (C_4H_8) is CH_2, while that of water is H_2O.

TIP
Calculation of the formula from percentage masses of the elements in a compound gives the empirical formula.

emulsion: a very fine suspension of droplets of one liquid in another liquid with which it is immiscible.
■ The droplets are so fine that they do not separate from suspension.
■ *e.g.* Milk is formed from fat droplets in water, and salad dressing from oil in water; emulsion paint is a suspension of fine droplets of paint in water.

endocrine gland: a structure that secretes a *hormone* into the bloodstream.
■ Most endocrine glands are stimulated into activity by hormones released from the pituitary gland, located at the base of the brain.
■ *e.g.* The ovary releases oestrogen and progesterone into the bloodstream at different stages of the *menstrual cycle*. The adrenal glands release *adrenaline* into the bloodstream to prepare the body for action.

e

endoscope: an instrument using *optical fibres* that allows doctors to see inside the hollow organs of a patient's body, such as the stomach, bowel and bladder.

endothermic reaction: a reaction that takes in energy as the reactants change into products.
■ The result is a fall in temperature.
■ *e.g.* The polymerisation of ethene to poly(ethene).

end-product inhibition: see *feedback inhibition*.

energy: the capacity of a body for doing work.
■ It has many forms: *electrical energy*, chemical energy, *potential energy, kinetic energy, heat* (thermal) energy, light energy, sound energy, nuclear energy. Changes of energy from one form to another make things happen. The principle of *conservation of energy* says that energy is neither lost nor gained. However, in most transfers some energy is lost to a less useful form, usually heat. Energy is measured in *joules* and *kilowatt hours*.

TIP Think of energy being needed to make this happen. The amount of energy converted is the *work done*.

energy level diagram: a diagram that shows the overall changes in energy during the course of a chemical reaction.
■ When bonds are broken in the reactants, energy is taken in. When bonds are formed in the products, energy is released.

energy resources: primary sources of energy that can be used for industry and for domestic needs.
■ *Fossil fuels* are easy to use but are forms of *non-renewable energy* and will eventually be used up. *Renewable energy* sources are more difficult to use but can be replaced.

enzyme: a protein that speeds up a chemical reaction in cells.
■ Each enzyme molecule catalyses a huge number of chemical reactions in a minute. Each type of reaction in cells requires a different enzyme because each enzyme can catalyse only one type of reaction. Enzyme molecules make very close contact with the molecules they work on and so the surface shapes of the enzyme's active site and the target molecule are very important. Anything that alters the surface shape of the enzyme, such as changes in pH or high temperature, will cause the molecule to become *denatured* and affect the enzyme's activity. Some changes can be reversed, but others are irreversible.
■ *e.g.* Digestive enzymes are secreted into the gut to break down large insoluble nutrient molecules to small soluble molecules that can pass through the gut wall into the blood. Digestive enzymes are named according to the compounds they degrade, so protein-degrading enzymes are proteases and starch-degrading enzymes are carbohydrases.

equation, chemical: a means of indicating the reactants and products of a chemical reaction by using chemical symbols and *formulae*.
■ The reactants are written on the left-hand side and the products on the right-hand side. The reacting proportions (stoichiometry) — how many units of each reactant and product are involved — are also shown.

equilibrium, chemical: an equilibrium that occurs when the rate of the forward change equals the rate of the backward change.
■ Most industrial reactions are based on equilibria and are known as reversible reactions.
■ *e.g.* Equilibria can occur either for a *physical change* (e.g. ice turning into water) or for a *chemical change* (e.g. the manufacture of ammonia from nitrogen and hydrogen).

equilibrium, mechanical: a state in which all forces are balanced so that an object remains at rest or moves with a steady velocity.
■ *e.g.* When you stand still your *weight* is balanced by the upwards force of the floor on your feet and you are in equilibrium. (See also *weightless*.) The weight of a parachutist is equal and opposite to the upwards force on the parachute so the parachutist is in equilibrium and falls with a fixed velocity called the *terminal velocity*.

ester: an organic compound that contains the R–C(=O)O–R′ group (where R′ is an organic group).
■ Esters smell fruity. They are made by the reaction of an *alcohol* with an organic acid and are used as solvents and in flavourings. Natural animal fats and vegetable oils contain the ester group. Esters can be broken down to alcohols and organic acids by boiling with sodium hydroxide solution.

ethane: a *hydrocarbon* with the formula C_2H_6, which is obtained as part of the *distillation* process of *crude oil*, and is also found in natural gas.
■ It is used as a fuel.

ethanoic acid (also called 'acetic acid'): an acid with the formula CH_3CO_2H.
■ Ethanoic acid can be made by the *oxidation* of *ethanol*. It is used industrially in the preparation of chemicals and in the manufacture of plastics. It is found as a 4% solution in vinegar.

ethanol: an alcohol with the formula CH_3CH_2OH.
■ It is a clear, colourless liquid which is toxic in large amounts. It can be prepared by the fermentation of sugars under anaerobic conditions using *yeast*. Industrially, it is made by the hydration of *ethene*, using steam and a *catalyst* of phosphoric acid at high temperatures. Ethanol can be used as a fuel, and as a solvent. It is also present in alcoholic drinks.

ethene: a gas with the formula C_4H_4.

■Ethene is obtained from the *distillation* of *crude oil*, and also by the *cracking* of oil. It is widely used to make the *polymer* poly(ethene), as well as ethanol.

eutrophication: a process that occurs in nutrient-rich bodies of water which can lead ultimately to the loss of oxygen-using organisms.

■Increased minerals in water from fertilisers, farm wastes and waste water allow algae to flourish and form an *algal bloom*. The algae block light needed by plants growing beneath them. When the algae and plants die, bacteria at the bottom of the pond decompose them, using dissolved oxygen in the process. This deprives other aquatic organisms of oxygen so they die in turn. The water quickly becomes anaerobic and only specialised organisms can survive.

evaporation: the process whereby a liquid turns into a gas, at a temperature below its boiling point.

■As the molecules with the highest speeds escape from the liquid surface, heat is taken from the liquid. Warming the liquid increases the rate of evaporation and is useful in concentrating solutions — and in drying clothes! It takes over five times as much heat to convert 1g of boiling water into steam as it takes to heat 1g of water from 0°C to 100°C.

■ *e.g.* Evaporation is widely used for concentrating solutions, or when growing crystals from saturated solutions. It is also used by the body to transfer heat to the environment through sweating.

evolution: changes in the genetic features of organisms over a long period of time.

■Evolution is the result of changes in features that are inherited, i.e. encoded in *genes*. These genes might be for physical structures, aspects of the organism's metabolism or a type of behaviour. *Natural selection* works on the features displayed by individuals; those with features that adapt them well to the environment are better able to reproduce and raise offspring. Over a period of time, the balance of genetic features shifts towards those that adapt a species to its local environment. In other environments other features may be more advantageous. New species arise as a result of populations of organisms adapting to the specific conditions within their local environment and becoming repro-ductively isolated. Changes in genetic material — *mutations* — contribute to the process of evolution.

exchange surface: a structure that is specialised to allow substances to pass into and out of an organism.

■ *e.g.* In the lungs, oxygen is exchanged for carbon dioxide across the walls of an *alveolus*. The surface of the alveolus is the exchange surface. In a leaf, the exchange surface is that of mesophyll cells, inside the leaf.

TIP   The leaf itself is not the exchange surface.

excretion: the removal of unwanted and potentially harmful material from the body. These substances are the result of living processes in the body.

■ The lungs and kidneys are both excretory organs. Carbon dioxide is generated by *respiration* in cells and transported by the blood to the lungs where it is excreted to the air. *Urea* is made in the liver from the breakdown of surplus amino acids. It is removed from blood by the kidneys and excreted in urine.

Do not confuse with egestion, which is the elimination of faeces from the gut.

exfoliation (also called 'onion-skin weathering'): the breaking away of the outer layer of rocks caused by the expansion and contraction of the rock due to extreme changes of temperature.

exothermic reaction: a reaction that gives out energy as the reactants change into products.

■ The result is a rise in temperature.

■ *e.g.* Respiration and combustion processes are examples of exothermic reactions.

expanding universe: the theory that the *universe* started with a *big bang* and has been expanding ever since.

■ This theory says that every part of the universe is moving away from every other part. It is supported by the *red shift* in the light from stars that are moving away from us. The further away they are, the faster they are moving and the greater the red shift.

extension: the stretch of a spring or wire that is under *tension.*

■ In a spring, the tension is proportional to the extension until the *elastic limit* is reached.

■ *e.g.* If a force of 6 N increases the length of a spring from 10 cm to 14 cm, the extension is 4 cm. A force of 3 N would stretch the spring to a length of 12 cm.

extinction: when all the members of a species of animal or plant have completely died out.

■ Huge numbers of species have evolved, flourished and become extinct during the Earth's history. Species become extinct when they can no longer live and breed successfully in their environment. This can be because of physical changes to their habitat or the activity of other species. There have been several mass extinctions in geological history when a large number of species disappeared in a fairly short time. These have spurred the *evolution* of new species. Today most species become extinct through human activity, particularly as a result of the destruction of habitat.

extrusive: a type of rock that has been expelled to the Earth's surface as lava, and has then cooled relatively quickly.

■ Extrusive *igneous rocks* always have small, interlocking crystals — basalt is one such example.

eye: a sense organ with receptors sensitive to light.

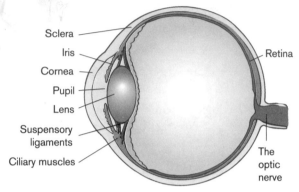

Sclera
Iris
Cornea
Pupil
Lens
Suspensory ligaments
Ciliary muscles
Retina
The optic nerve

The tough outer sclera has a transparent region at the front – the cornea.

The muscular iris controls the size of the pupil and hence the amount of light falling on the light-sensitive retina.

The optic nerve carries impulses from the retina to the brain.

The lens is held in position by suspensory ligaments and ciliary muscles. The shape of the lens can be altered by these muscles.

F1 hybrid: the offspring of a mating (cross) between two homozygous (pure-breeding) parents (see *homozygote*) that differ in one particular genetic feature.
■ The feature is carried by a pair of *genes*, and exists in two forms, or *alleles* (for example, wrinkled peas and round peas). Each parent has alleles for one version only — they are pure breeding. The offspring inherit one gene from each parent and therefore carry both versions of the feature — they are hybrids. Individuals from this first generation are described as F1 hybrids.
■ *e.g.* Plant breeders develop F1 hybrids as the combination of features from two different strains may result in better quality plants or new colours.

faraday: the unit of electric charge corresponding to 96 500 coulombs.
■ This is the amount of charge carried by 1 mole of electrons.

fat: see *lipid*.

fault: a fracture in the Earth's crust along which some displacement has taken place.
■ One part may drop relative to the other part, one part may be pushed up or the two parts may slide past each other (known as a transform fault). When stress is relieved at a fault an *earthquake* can result. Such movements are often associated with *plate tectonics*.

feedback inhibition (also called 'end-product inhibition'): a control mechanism for body processes in which increasing amounts of a product stop the processes that make it.
■ It is used to control hormonal processes and reactions catalysed by enzymes. Accumulation of a product in a cell stops an enzyme working in an early stage of the production process.

fermentation: a process used by bacteria and fungi to release energy from foods without using oxygen.
■ In many cases this is a form of *anaerobic respiration* and generates ethanol or lactic acid as an end product. Some organisms produce other organic acids as end products, such as butyric acid.

f

■ *e.g. Yeast* ferments sugar to make *ethanol* in brewing. Ethanol can be distilled from solution if it is needed in the pure form.

TIP In industrial processes, fermentation is often used to describe any process that uses microorganisms to make a product, even if they use oxygen in respiration.

fermenter: a large vessel used to grow microorganisms in a completely controlled environment.

■ The microorganisms are provided with nutrients, stirred, aerated if necessary, and kept at the best pH and temperature for growth. After a suitable time, the process can be stopped and the microbes, or any product they have made, can be harvested from the fermenter.

■ *e.g.* Fermenters are used to grow the microorganisms that make antibiotics and washing powder enzymes.

fertilisation: the process in which a male *gamete* combines with a female *gamete* to produce a *zygote*. This can then develop into a new individual organism.

■ In humans and other animals, a sperm cell combines with an egg. In plants a nucleus from the pollen grain combines with a nucleus in the ovule. Fertilisation brings together unique combinations of genes — an important feature of *sexual reproduction*.

fertiliser: a substance that provides nutrients to the soil to promote plant growth.

■ Most inorganic fertilisers contain sources of nitrogen (ammonium salts, including nitrate), phosphorus (phosphate rock) and potassium (potassium chloride). The ratios of each of these chemicals will vary depending on the precise needs of the plants concerned (see *NPK ratio*). Organic fertilisers include manure (farm animal waste, often mixed with straw) and garden compost. The quantity of each chemical nutrient is very variable.

TIP Nitrate (NO_3^-) is the same, whether it comes from inorganic or organic fertiliser.

fertility drug: a *hormone* preparation used to stimulate ovulation.

■ Women may be unable to conceive a child because of a problem within the reproductive system. Fertility drugs are used to stimulate the production of eggs from a woman's ovaries. The released eggs can be collected surgically and mixed with sperm. A different hormone treatment is used to prepare the woman to receive fertilised eggs, which are introduced into the oviducts.

fetus: a young, developing mammal, bird or reptile from the point at which bones and organs start to form. A human embryo becomes a fetus at about 7 weeks when bone cells start to develop.

filament lamp: an electric lamp with a fine tungsten filament in a glass bulb. The bulb is either evacuated or filled with an inert gas.

■ An electric current heats the tungsten near to its melting point and it emits a warm white light. However, most of the electrical energy is transformed to *heat* and only a small amount to light. In low-energy lamps, which do not use hot filaments, a much smaller fraction of the electrical energy is transformed to heat.

TIP

The hotter the filament the higher is its resistance, the whiter its light, the higher its *efficiency* and the shorter is the life of the lamp.

filtration: the separation of small, insoluble particles from a liquid using physical means.
■ A filter paper has microscopic holes which trap the particles and prevent them from passing through with the liquid. The liquid that passes through the filter paper is known as the filtrate, while the solid that remains on the paper is known as the residue.

fission: the disintegration of a heavy atomic *nucleus* into two or more lighter particles.
■ The disintegration can be spontaneous or, in a nuclear reactor, induced by bombardment with neutrons. In each case, nuclear energy is released in the form of *heat*. (See *chain reaction*.)

flaccid: a term describing the water content of a plant cell or tissue. A flaccid cell has relatively little water, so the cell membrane does not push against the cell wall. As a result, the cells and tissues are floppy, in contrast to when the cells are *turgid*. When cells are flaccid, the plant wilts.

flame: the combusting gases above a substance that is burning.
■ The colour of a flame can be used to give an indication of the number of carbon atoms present if the substance is organic (the more yellow the flame, the more carbon atoms there are). If there is a metal present, the flame might be coloured. Copper produces a turquoise flame, potassium a lilac flame and strontium a red flame. If oxygen, heat or the fuel is removed then the flame will go out.

foetus: see *fetus*.

fold: the bending of the crust of the Earth due to pressures caused by colliding continental plates.
■ The two commonest types of fold are synclines and anticlines.

force: a pull or a push, measured in *newtons* (N).
■ If a force acting on an object is an *unbalanced force* it will cause the object to undergo *acceleration*. If forces on an object are *balanced forces* the object will be in *equilibrium*. The force in newtons = the mass in kg × the acceleration in m/s^2. $F = ma$.

formula: a series of symbols that gives the elements present in the substance.
■ A formula gives the number of atoms present within a molecule, or the ratio of the atoms present if the substance is ionic.

f

■ *e.g.* The formula of water is H_2O, implying that there are two hydrogen atoms and one oxygen atom within a molecule of water. The formula for the ionic compound sodium chloride (NaCl) implies that the sodium and chloride ions are present in a one-to-one ratio.

formula mass (also called 'relative formula mass'): the mass of a molecule compared with $\frac{1}{12}$ of the mass of an atom of carbon-12. It is obtained by adding together the relative atomic masses of the atoms within the molecule according to the written formula.

■ *e.g.* Calcium carbonate ($CaCO_3$) has a formula mass of $40 + 12 + 3(16) = 100$.

fossil: the preserved evidence of a long-dead animal or plant.

■ Fossils can be body parts or evidence of activity, such as tracks, burrows, nests or teeth marks. Most fossils are made of the hard parts of dead animals after they have become covered in sediments and subsequently impregnated with minerals.

fossil fuel: a fuel made from the remains of plants and animals that were buried millions of years ago.

■ Fossil fuels can be used to provide energy or as a source of other chemicals. However, they are a *non-renewable energy* resource due to the long time needed to form them.

■ *e.g.* Coal, oil and natural gas are the commonest fossil fuels.

fractional distillation: the process used to separate mixtures of liquids with fairly close boiling points.

■ The mixture of liquids is boiled and passed into a fractionation tower. Here the vapours are repeatedly condensed and reboiled. The more volatile liquid eventually emerges from the top of the tower and can be condensed.

■ *e.g.* Crude oil is separated by fractional distillation on an industrial scale. This allows each of its separate components to be tapped off.

Frasch process: a process used to extract water-soluble solids from deep underground, without the need for mining.

■ Three concentric tubes are driven into the deposit. Superheated water and compressed air are passed down two of them. The solid dissolves and is forced up the third tube and can be recovered.

■ *e.g.* Sodium chloride and sulphur can be extracted in this way.

free electron: an electron that is not directly attached to any particular atom or ion but is able to move between them.

■ Metals contain a regular lattice of metal cations with free electrons acting as an electronic glue holding them all together. It is the free electrons that enable the metal to conduct electricity and heat.

freeze–thaw: a process that results in the weathering of rocks.

■ Water droplets trapped in a rock crevice expand when the water freezes, forcing the crevice apart. When the water melts it can penetrate further into the crack and so the next time it freezes it forces the rock even further apart. Eventually the segment of rock flakes off.

freezing: the conversion of a liquid into a solid. Freezing occurs at a definite temperature for each substance, known as its *freezing point*.

freezing point: the temperature at which a substance changes from a liquid to a solid. (See *melting point*.)

frequency: the number of oscillations per second of a *wave* or any oscillating object, measured in *hertz* (Hz).
- 1 Hz is a frequency of 1 cycle per second.
- *e.g.* The national grid provides us with *alternating current* with a frequency of 50 Hz. *Sound waves* have frequencies between 20 and 20 000 Hz. *Ultrasonic waves* have frequencies above 20 000 Hz and usually of a few MHz. *Electromagnetic waves* have frequencies from 100 kHz (radio) to 10^{23} Hz (gamma rays).

TIP The **LOwer** the frequency, the **LOnger** the *wavelength*. See *speed of a wave*.

friction: a force between two surfaces, or between air and a solid object, which opposes their relative motion.
- Friction causes energy to be transformed to *heat* and can wear out the surfaces involved. It can be reduced by lubrication. An air cushion, as used in a hovercraft, can reduce friction to a low value. Air friction can also be reduced by streamlining.

froth flotation: the process used to separate fragments of mineral ores from the unwanted bedrock.
- Powdered rock is added to water and a special detergent added. Air is blown through the mixture. The mineral sticks to the bubbles and can be skimmed from the surface, while the unwanted material sinks and can be discarded.

fuel: a substance that can be economically burned to provide useful energy.
- *e.g.* Petrol, kerosene and diesel oil are very compact *fossil fuels* which provide energy for most of our transport. Nuclear fuel can also provide energy by the radioactive decay of uranium or plutonium atoms.

fungus: an organism usually made up of thread-like structures, or hyphae, with cell walls made of substances different from cellulose. Fungi do not contain chlorophyll.
- Toadstools and mushrooms are spore-producing structures arising from underground hyphae. Some produce *antibiotics*; some are important as *decomposers*.
- *e.g.* Yeast, which is used in bread and *alcohol* production.

fuse: a thin piece of wire that melts when the current through it is too great, disconnecting the circuit and preventing damage. (See *circuit breaker*.)
- 13-amp *plugs* use cartridge fuses of 3A, 5A up to a maximum of 13A.

galaxy: a large collection of *stars* held together by *gravity.*
■ The Sun is one of around 100000 stars in the spiral galaxy called the Milky Way. See also *nebula.*

galvanise: to coat a metal with a thin layer of zinc.
■ The zinc is unaffected by air and water and so prevents both of them from coming in contact with the underlying metal and causing it to rust.
■ *e.g.* Steel is often galvanised.

gamete: a sex cell, carrying half the number of *chromosomes* found in body cells.
■ Gametes are made in specialised organs by a form of cell division called *meiosis.* In animals, male sex cells are called sperm and female sex cells are eggs or ova (sing. ovum). Plants do not form separate individual sex cells; they are carried in pollen (male) and ovules (female).

gamma rays: *electromagnetic waves* of very high *frequency* and very short *wavelength* emitted by unstable *nuclei.*
■ Gamma rays cause less *ionisation* than *alpha* or *beta particles* but are very penetrating; they can be reduced by thick lead or concrete. They are dangerous but are useful for killing bacteria and sterilising medical equipment.

TIP The more ionisation, the easier it is to stop the radiation.

gas: a state of matter in which all the particles of a substance are moving freely and capable of filling any space into which they are placed.
■ Natural gas (methane, CH_4) is formed with *crude oil.* It is one of the products of the anaerobic decay of plants and animals that died millions of years ago.

gene: a length of *DNA* that encodes the structure of a protein.
■ A gene is the smallest unit of inheritance. The protein it encodes plays a role in the development of an inherited feature. Each gene is composed of a sequence of bases, interpreted in groups of three. Each group signifies a particular amino acid to be incorporated into a protein. So, the sequence of groups of three bases signifies the sequence of amino acids to be incorporated into the protein.

g

The definition of gene has changed as more research has been carried out on genetics. Many biology textbooks, especially older ones, describe a gene as a unit of inherited information that controls a particular characteristic, such as eye colour. This definition is part of *Mendelian genetics*, worked out long before *DNA* was described. Genes come in different versions or *alleles*. They can be affected by *mutation*.

generator: a machine that converts mechanical energy into electrical energy.
■ Generators produce either alternating current *(a.c. generators)* or direct current *(d.c. generators)*.

genetic modification: a technique of altering the genetic constitution of an organism by introducing genes from another organism or changing existing genes.
■ Genes are transferred into bacteria or yeast, to enable them to make useful substances they could not previously make. Desirable genes, such as those for making insulin, are prepared and inserted into a *vector* to carry them into new host cells. Bacterial plasmids, which are small loops of DNA, are often used. Suitable host bacteria take in the plasmids, and use the new genes to make the new product.
■ *e.g.* Modified bacteria are used to make human insulin and growth hormone, and modified yeast makes chymosin which is used in cheese making.

genotype: the total number and types of genes that an organism possesses.
■ The genotype includes any *recessive alleles* that an organism has as well as those that are expressed.

geological time: relates periods in the Earth's prehistory with approximate dates.

Period	Time (millions of years ago)	Era
Quaternary		Cenozoic
Tertiary		
Cretaceous	100	Mesozoic
Jurassic		
Triassic	200	
Permian		Paleozoic
Carboniferous		
Devonian	300	
Silurian	400	
Ordovician		
Cambrian	500 600	
Precambrian	700 3000	Archaeozoic

g

geostationary orbit: an *orbit* around the Earth that keeps a *satellite* above a fixed point on the equator.
- The satellite orbits the Earth once every 24 hours in the same direction as the rotation of the Earth. To do this it has to be about 36 000 km above the Earth's surface and this causes a delay of about $\frac{1}{5}$ of a second between transmission and reception of a message.
- *e.g.* These satellites are used as *communications satellites*. Satellite aerial dishes aim directly at one of these satellites which appear to be stationary relative to the Earth. (See also *monitoring satellite*.)

TIP
Geostationary satellites have to orbit above the equator.

geothermal energy: *heat* energy that is obtained from the hot interior of the Earth.
- This is a form of *renewable energy* as radioactivity within the Earth is continually producing more heat energy. It is practical to use this energy only in places where the hot layers are near to the surface.

giant structure: the regular, three-dimensional arrangement of particles in space.
- The particles may be *atoms* (such as carbon in diamond), *ions* (such as sodium and chloride ions in a salt crystal) or *molecules* (such as sucrose molecules in a sugar crystal).

global warming: the effect of gases in the Earth's atmosphere causing the radiation from the Sun to be trapped, in the so-called *greenhouse effect*, thereby increasing the temperature of the world.
- It is thought that an increase in the world's overall temperature might cause the polar ice caps to melt and therefore cause flooding of low-lying land.

glomerulus: a cluster of capillaries at the entry to a kidney tubule.
- The capillaries are tiny and blood passes through them under very high pressure. Plasma, carrying dissolved substances, is forced through the walls into the kidney tubule, but blood cells and large molecules such as proteins remain in the capillary. The process is called *ultrafiltration*.

glucose: a sugar with the formula $C_6H_{12}O_6$.
- Glucose is a white, crystalline solid. It is produced in plants during the process of *photosynthesis* and is found in all plants and animals where it is used up during respiration to produce energy.

glycogen: A carbohydrate that is a polymer made from glucose subunits which acts as an energy store in animals.
- Glycogen is found in liver and muscle cells.

grain size: grains form in a metal when it cools. Slow cooling results in the formation of large grains (regular arrangements of atoms), whereas fast cooling results in very small grains.

g

■ Small grains result in harder, stronger metals. Grain size is important when fabricating metal objects so that they are suitable for their intended stresses and strains.

granite: an intrusive *igneous rock*.

■ Granite forms when molten magma cools within the Earth. The molten rock is insulated and so cools slowly, resulting in the formation of large, interlocking grains, usually containing quartz crystals.

graphite: an *allotrope* of carbon.

■ The carbon atoms are arranged in six-membered rings in sheets. These sheets can slide over each other — graphite is used as a lubricant. Free electrons can move between the sheets, thereby allowing the graphite to conduct electricity. It is often used as an electrode material, for example in dry cells, and for *brushes* in electrical machines.

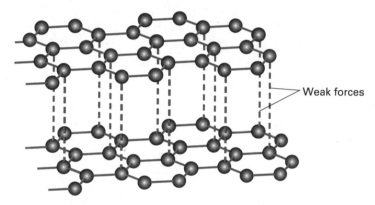

Weak forces

gravitational field strength: the strength of the gravitational field of the Earth, symbol g.

■ This field causes all masses on the Earth's surface to be attracted towards the centre of the Earth. It has a strength of about $g = 9.81$ N/kg on the Earth's surface but it is slightly greater at the poles and slightly less at the equator. A simpler value of $g = 10$ N/kg is often used in calculations. The value of g lessens at distances further from the Earth's surface, but does not reach zero.

■ *e.g.* A *mass* of 2 kg is attracted towards the Earth by a force of 2 kg × 10 N/kg = 20 N. So the mass has a *weight* of 20 N.

gravitational potential energy: the energy a *mass* has on account of its height above the Earth's surface.

■ When a mass is raised its gravitational potential energy is increased by an amount given by its *weight* (mg) multiplied by the increase in height (h).

■ *e.g.* A mass of 4 kg is raised through a distance of 3 m. Its potential energy is increased by 4 kg × 10 N/kg × 3 m = 120 Nm = 120 J.

g

Remember that a change in gravitational potential energy is *mgh*.

gravity: the force of nature that causes any two masses to be attracted to each other.

■ The force is significant only when one (or both) of the masses is very large. The attraction between two people is negligible but the attraction between the Earth and a person is about 700 N.

Gravity works both ways. The Earth is attracting the person down with a force of 700 N and the person is also attracting the Earth up with a force of 700 N. (See *Newton's third law*.)

greenhouse effect: the trapping of energy within the Earth's atmosphere, resulting in *global warming*.

■ Radiation from the Sun passes through the atmosphere. It is absorbed by the Earth and re-radiated as infrared which can be absorbed by gases in the atmosphere (carbon dioxide, methane, water vapour etc.). The gases gain energy and so the atmosphere warms up.

greenhouse gas: gas in the atmosphere that absorbs infrared radiation.

■ Greenhouse gases act as an insulating blanket above the Earth's surface and trap heat being re-radiated from the Earth. The main greenhouse gases are carbon dioxide, methane and water vapour. As the quantity of carbon dioxide in the atmosphere has increased over the last century, the atmosphere has warmed and seems likely to become warmer.

group: a vertical column of elements in the periodic table. Elements in the same group have the same number of outer electrons.

■ The chemical properties of the elements in a particular group are similar. Groups are numbered (left to right across the periodic table) from 1 to 7; the last group (the inert gases) is group 0.

guard cell: one of a pair of cells that changes shape to open or close a *stoma* (pl. stomata) on a leaf.

■ The shape change in guard cells is linked to the composition of the fluids inside the cells. In daylight, water is drawn into the cells by *osmosis*; the cells expand and become *turgid*. The walls of the guard cells are slightly thicker near the opening so they flex less when the cell enlarges. This results in the two cells curving away from each other, leaving a gap between for air to enter and leave. At night, the cells lose water, become *flaccid*, and the gap closes.

Haber process: the industrial manufacture of ammonia.

■Nitrogen (from the air) and hydrogen (from methane and steam) are mixed in the presence of an iron *catalyst* at 450°C and 250 atmospheres pressure. Ammonia is formed with about 18% yield. It is liquefied and drained off while unreacted gases are recycled.

habitat: the place or environment in which a particular organism lives.

haemoglobin: a protein found in red blood cells which is responsible for transporting oxygen.

■In the lungs, haemoglobin links to oxygen to make oxyhaemoglobin. Blood's bright red colour is due to oxyhaemoglobin. It releases oxygen in the tissues and the colour darkens. Iron is needed to make haemoglobin. If the body is short of iron, insufficient red blood cells are made, resulting in anaemia.

half-life: the time it takes for the activity of a radioactive substance, and also its mass, to be halved.

■The half-life depends on the element and can be anything from a fraction of a second to millions of years.

■ *e.g.* 4 g of $^{241}_{94}$ plutonium decay, emitting *alpha* and *beta particles,* and become 2 g of this plutonium after 13.27 years. In another 13.27 years there will be 1g of the plutonium.

halogen: the common name for group 7 elements in the periodic table: fluorine, chlorine, bromine, iodine and astatine.

■Halogens have seven electrons in their outermost electronic shell. They are all reactive non-metals whose reactivity increases going up the group. Halogens exist as diatomic molecules. When ionised they all gain one electron to form the X^- halide ion.

hard water: water that does not form a lather with soap.

■It contains dissolved calcium and magnesium carbonates, hydrogencarbonates and sulphates. When heated, hard water deposits scale which can clog pipes. It is, however, good to drink as it contains minerals required by the body.

h

heat: a form of *energy* that raises the *temperature* of an object.

■ The *kinetic theory* says that the heat energy (thermal energy) in an object is contained in the rapid motion of its *molecules*.

heat transfer: heat energy can be transferred from one place to another by *conduction, convection, radiation* and by *evaporation* and condensation.

herbicide: a chemical that kills vegetation.

■ Some herbicides are very similar to plant *auxins*; they damage the plants' ability to control their growth, eventually killing them. Farmers use herbicides in their fields to kill emerging weeds that could compete with crops for light, water and minerals and so reduce the yield.

hertz: the unit for *frequency*; it gives the number of cycles or oscillations per second.

heterozygote: an individual with two different *alleles* for a particular inherited character.

■ Inherited features are carried as genes. Variations of the feature are called alleles. Individuals can inherit different alleles for a feature from each of their parents.

■ *e.g.* Someone with blond hair may also carry an allele for red hair.

TIP

In pea plants where the letter T represents the tall allele and t represents the short allele, the heterozygote is represented by Tt.

homeostasis: the process of regulating the internal environment of the body within very narrow limits.

■ Body temperature and the composition of blood and tissue fluids are carefully regulated so that cells can work at peak efficiency. Cells can be damaged if their environment changes significantly. There are receptors throughout the body monitoring aspects of metabolism. These pass impulses to the brain where much homeostatic activity is coordinated.

■ *e.g.* If the body is too hot, the rise in blood temperature is detected by the brain which causes *vasodilation* in the skin and an increase in sweating in the body to increase heat transfer to the environment. The brain also instigates behaviour to cool the body, such as shade seeking and removing clothing.

homologous chromosomes: a matched pair of chromosomes.

■ Homologous chromosomes look the same under a microscope and carry thousands of *genes*. Humans have 22 homologous pairs of chromosomes and a pair of sex chromosomes, which may differ. When sex cells (*gametes*) such as sperm and eggs are made in *meiosis*, homologous chromosomes separate so that only one from each pair enters a sex cell. The pair is restored when a sperm carrying one chromosome of a pair fertilises an egg carrying a similar chromosome.

homologous series: a group of organic compounds whose chemical formulae differ by one carbon and two hydrogen atoms.

■ Members of a homologous series have the same chemical properties, while their physical properties will change in a regular manner.

■ *e.g.* The *alkenes*: methane (CH_4), ethane (C_2H_6) and propane (C_3H_8).

homozygote: an individual that has two of the same *alleles* for an inherited feature. (See *heterozygote*.)

hormone: a chemical released from a gland that regulates the activity of organs in other parts of the body. Plants produce hormones, but not from specialised glands.

■ Hormones control body activity and are effective in minute quantities. They are released from *endocrine glands* directly into the bloodstream, which conveys them to target organs. Unlike nerve action, hormone action is usually slow, long-lasting and can involve several organs. Plants produce substances such as *auxins*, which are similar to hormones and lead to long-lasting responses.

■ *e.g.* Human growth hormone, released from the pituitary gland at the base of the brain, leads to growth of bones, muscle and cartilage. *Anti-diuretic hormone (ADH)* from the pituitary conserves water by causing its return from the kidney tubules into the bloodstream.

humus: decayed remains of animal and plant material in the soil.

■ Decomposers in soil break down plant and animal material to minute fragments and release many types of molecule into the soil. Humus is a brownish-black mixture of material that absorbs water and helps to stick soil particles together. It also slowly releases minerals into the soil. Farmers and gardeners add manure or compost to the soil to increase the humus content, thereby improving the water-holding capacity, mineral content and soil structure.

Huntington's disease: an inherited disorder of the nervous system.

■ Huntington's disease is caused by a dominant allele and can therefore be passed on by one parent who has the disorder. It develops later in life, by which time the sufferer will have passed the disorder on to any children.

hydraulic systems: mechanical systems that are linked by pipes and are driven by liquid at a high *pressure*.

■ The system has a pump with a *master piston* which produces the high pressure liquid. This is then piped to one or more *slave pistons* which produce forces that are proportional to the areas of their pistons.

$$\text{force on the slave piston} = \frac{\text{force on the master piston} \times \text{the area of the slave piston}}{\text{area of the master piston}}$$

h

$$\text{pressure of the liquid} = \frac{\text{force on the master piston}}{\text{area of the master piston}}$$

hydrocarbon: an organic compound made up of carbon and hydrogen atoms only.

■ Hydrocarbons burn in excess oxygen to give carbon dioxide and water only. They can undergo substitution reactions with halogens in the presence of ultraviolet light, and can be cracked to give shorter-chained alkanes and alkenes.

■ *e.g.* Butane (C_4H_{10}) and decane ($C_{10}H_{22}$).

hydroelectric power: electric power produced by moving water that drives a turbine which then turns a *generator*.

■ This is a *renewable energy* source. It can be produced by water from a high reservoir falling through pipes (*potential energy* changing to *electrical energy*), or by river water flowing through a turbine (*kinetic energy* changing to electrical energy). (See also *pumped storage* and *tidal power*.)

hydrogen: the simplest element known — made up of one proton and one electron.

■ Hydrogen is a colourless gas which is less dense than air. It can be made by the action of acids on metals or, industrially, by the action of methane with steam. It is highly reactive and can form explosive mixtures with air. Hydrogen atoms can lose an electron to form the H^+ *cation*. However, they can also gain an electron to form the H^- *anion* when combined with reactive metals.

hydrogenation: the addition of hydrogen to an organic compound.

■ Industrially, this is used in the preparation of margarine — hydrogen gas is combined with carbon–carbon *double bonds* in oils and fats, in the presence of a nickel catalyst.

hydrogen chloride: a colourless gas that is readily soluble in water, forming hydrochloric acid.

■ Hydrochloric acid is a strong acid — the HCl molecules totally dissociate in water, forming H^+ ions and Cl^- ions. Industrially, hydrogen chloride gas is prepared by the direct combination of hydrogen and chlorine. In the lab it is made by the reaction of concentrated sulphuric acid with sodium chloride.

hydrogen peroxide: a colourless liquid, H_2O_2, which readily decomposes to give water and oxygen.

■ Manganese dioxide (MnO_2) is commonly used as a *catalyst* for this de-composition.

hydrolysis: the reaction of a compound with water.

■ It is the reverse of a condensation reaction.

■ *e.g.* During digestion, large macromolecules are hydrolysed into their building blocks by reaction with water (e.g. carbohydrates into glucose, and proteins into amino acids).

hydroxonium ion: the *cation* that forms (H_3O^+) when an acid dissolves in water.
■ It is formed when a proton from the acid joins with a molecule of water:

$$HCl + H_2O \longrightarrow H_3O^+ + Cl^-$$

hypothalamus: a region of the brain that is involved in *hormone* production as well as nervous activity.
■ The hormones it secretes pass down into the pituitary gland for release into the bloodstream. Many of them influence the activity of *endocrine glands*. Links between nerves and hormones make it possible to coordinate responses that involve internal body changes and changes in behaviour, such as the increase in alertness and arousal of the 'fight or flight' response.

igneous rock: rock formed by the cooling of molten *magma*.

■Igneous rocks are hard and crystalline. If they form within the Earth they are called intrusive and have large crystal sizes (e.g. granite). If they are formed on the surface they are called extrusive and have small crystal sizes (e.g. basalt).

immune system: any mechanism the body uses to defend itself against infectious microorganisms and other foreign material.

■The immune system has two components — one involves innate immunity; the other is acquired. Innate immunity includes all barriers to microbe entry (skin, enzymes in tears, mucus, stomach acid and cilia in the trachea and its branches) and some general purpose responses by white blood cells. The immune system is also responsible for acquired immunity. This involves *lymph* nodes and bone marrow, the *white blood cells* they make, and *antibodies* made by white blood cells. White blood cells recognise and take in foreign material to destroy it. They also make antibodies that hinder the progress of an infection. A memory of the infecting organism is made, resulting in a rapid response if the infecting organism ever reappears. The immune system also recognises other forms of foreign material, such as pollen and rogue or damaged cells, and destroys them.

immunity: see *immune system*.

impulse (biology): a wave of excitation that passes along a nerve cell.

■It enters via dendrites, passes through the cell body and out along the axon. At the end of the axon it passes across *synapses* to other nerve cells or to muscle or gland cells.

impulse (physics): the product of a force multiplied by the time during which it acts, measured in kg m/s.

■In practice, impulses are produced by large forces acting for very short times and it is difficult to measure either the force or the time. Impulses are usually calculated from the change of momentum that they cause:

$$\text{Impulse } Ft = mv - mu$$

■ *e.g.* A 2 kg trolley at rest moves off at 3 m/s after being struck by a hammer. The hammer blow gave an impulse of 6 kg m/s to the trolley.

indicator: acid–base indicators are used to give information on the *pH* of solutions.

■ Indicators change colour depending on the pH.

■ *e.g.* Phenolphthalein is colourless in acid and purple in alkali; litmus is red in acid and blue in alkali; universal indicator solution is red at pH 1, green at pH 7 and blue at pH 14.

induced voltage: the voltage (actually an *electromotive force*) produced by *electromagnetic induction* in a conductor or coil.

inert: resistant to chemical reactions.

■ *e.g.* The noble gases (group 0), and some metals such as gold and platinum.

infrared: invisible *electromagnetic waves* with wavelengths longer than visible red radiation and shorter than *radio waves*.

■ The Sun radiates energy in all parts of the *electromagnetic spectrum,* but like other glowing objects it radiates most energy in the *infrared* range.

■ *e.g.* Infrared waves are used to transmit signals from remote control units to television sets. They are also used to 'see' through fog as the longer waves are scattered much less by water droplets than are visible light waves. See also *diffraction.*

inherited disorder: any disorder that is inherited, as opposed to a disease depending on infectious agents or environmental factors.

■ *e.g. cystic fibrosis, Huntington's disease, sickle-cell anaemia.*

inorganic: defining the large class of those compounds that do not contain carbon atoms held together by carbon–carbon covalent bonds.

■ *e.g.* Examples of inorganic compounds are water (H_2O), sodium chloride (NaCl) and carbon dioxide (CO_2).

insulator, electrical: any substance that prevents the flow of electricity.

■ *e.g.* Fortunately, air is a good insulator. Plastics are commonly used for rigid insulators. PVC (polyvinyl chloride, poly(chloroethene)) is used for most low-voltage cables. Overhead high-voltage cables use porcelain and glass insulators and air.

insulator, heat: any substance that restricts the flow of *heat* from a hot place to a cold one.

■ Gases are the best insulators if *convection* can be prevented.

■ *e.g.* Substances such as expanded polystyrene, which has millions of small pockets of air and not much solid material, make good insulators. Others are wool, glass wool and fibre glass. Wood and plastics are fair insulators and so make good handles for saucepans.

insulin: a *hormone* that regulates the concentration of glucose in the blood.

■ Insulin is produced by the pancreas and released into the blood when blood sugar levels rise, usually when digesting and absorbing a meal. Insulin enables glucose to enter cells. Cells in the liver and muscles can store the glucose they take in as *glycogen*. When the blood glucose concentration falls, glucose is released from these stores for use. People with *diabetes* have problems making sufficient insulin to control their blood sugar.

intensive farming: keeping farm animals in a controlled environment inside buildings to optimise their growth for meat or other products.

■ Chickens, pigs and other animals are confined indoors in pens or cages and fed carefully determined diets. This reduces energy transferred to the environment through movement, foraging and maintaining body temperature. Food concentrates provide balanced nutrients with the minimum of waste. Automated machinery can be used to dispense food and water, maintain temperature and ventilation. Large numbers of animals and eggs can be produced from a small, perhaps poor quality, piece of land. There are many welfare issues raised by intensive farming, particularly the animals' lack of freedom to express natural behaviour.

intrusive: rock formed beneath the surface of the Earth.

■ Molten *magma* cools slowly, as it is insulated by the Earth, forming large crystals of hard rock. The forming of one mineral within another mineral vein is also an example of intrusion.

■ *e.g.* Granite.

ion: a particle that has gained *electrons* (forming a negative ion) or has lost electrons (forming a positive ion).

ion exchange: a technique for treating substances that involves the swapping of one ion for another.

■ This takes place on resin-coated beads (ion-exchange resin). It is used to remove calcium and magnesium ions from hard water and replace them with sodium ions, which do not cause hardness. Ion exchange is also used in the purification of radioactive substances. Some water companies use it to remove nitrates from drinking water.

ionic bond: a bond formed between a metal and a non-metal when the metal transfers electrons to the non-metallic element so that both attain a full, stable, outer shell of electrons.

■ The bond is not localised between the atoms concerned — it is non-directional.

■ *e.g.* The three-dimensional lattice of sodium and chloride ions in sodium chloride is held together by ionic bonds.

ionic equation: an equation that contains only the ions that react and undergo change in a chemical reaction.

■ Ions that do not take part in the reaction are known as spectator ions.

■ *e.g.* For the reaction between lead nitrate solution and sodium chloride solution the ionic equation is:

$$Pb^{2+}(aq) + 2\,Cl^-(aq) \longrightarrow PbCl_2(s) \ .$$

The sodium and nitrate ions are spectator ions.

ionisation: the process of making ions (charged atoms or molecules).

■ It can occur when an acid dissolves in water (e.g. $HCl + H_2O \longrightarrow H_3O^+ + Cl^-$), or when ionic compounds are formed (e.g. $2Na + Cl_2 \longrightarrow 2Na^+Cl^-$). It is also produced by electric sparks and by *ionising radiation*.

ionising radiation: any *electromagnetic wave* (*X-ray* or *gamma ray*) or *alpha-* or *beta particle* that can produce pairs of positive and negative *ions* on passing through a substance.

isomer: a substance that has the same molecular formula but a different structural formula (arrangement of atoms) as another substance.

■ Isomers can have different chemical and physical properties from each other.

■ *e.g.* C_5H_{12} has three isomers:

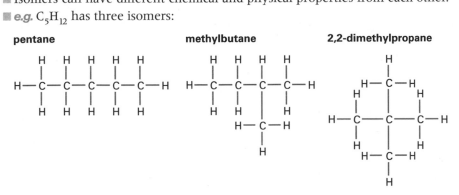

pentane   **methylbutane**   **2,2-dimethylpropane**

isotope: another form of the same element that has a different number of neutrons in the nucleus.

■ Isotopes differ in atomic mass but have the same chemical properties.

■ *e.g.* Hydrogen (1 proton, 1 electron, 0 neutrons), deuterium (1 proton, 1 electron, 1 neutron) and tritium (1 proton, 1 electron, 2 neutrons).

joint: where components of exo- or endoskeletons meet.
- Joints can be immovable (e.g. between skull bones), moveable within tight limits (e.g. between vertebrae) or freely moveable (e.g. hinged joints or ball-and-socket joints). Moveable joints involve lever systems moved by *antagonistic muscles*.

joule: the unit of *energy*, symbol J. It is the energy transferred when a *force* of 1 newton moves through a distance of 1 metre in the direction of the force.
- When a force moves, the energy transferred in joules = force in newtons × distance in metres, $E = Fd$. In electricity, energy transferred in joules = power in watts × time in seconds, $E = Pt$. The energy transferred to heat by a resistor can also be calculated as $E = I^2Rt$.

joule meter: an electrical meter which continuously measures current and voltage and, by adding values of *IVt*, displays the total energy used in joules.
- A kilowatt hour meter works in the same way, but displays the energy in *kilowatt hours*. The meter needs three connections to make the measurements.

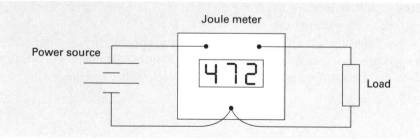

karyotype: the number, types and staining patterns of chromosomes found in the ordinary cells of an animal or plant.

■ Every individual in an animal or plant species has the same number of chromosomes in homologous pairs. These are visible during cell division but randomly arranged. The chromosomes in dividing cells are analysed and matched according to size, chromosome shape and stained bands and compared with standard preparations. This is often used medically in order to look for abnormalities.

kelvin: the *SI unit* of *temperature*.

■ An interval of 1 K is the same as an interval of 1 °C. *Absolute zero* is 0 K and −273 °C. The melting point of ice is 273 K and 0 °C.

TIP Kelvin temperatures do not need the word degree or the symbol °.

ketone: an organic compound that contains the −(C=O)− group.

■ Ketones are usually sweet-smelling liquids or low melting-point solids.

■ *e.g.* The commonest ketone is propanone (acetone, $CH_3C(O)CH_3$), which is used as a solvent.

kilowatt hour (also called 'unit'): the energy transferred when a *power* of 1 kilowatt is used for 1 hour.

■ The term 'unit' (short for Board of Trade Unit) is used by suppliers of electricity when they charge for electrical energy.

$$1 \text{ kilowatt hour} = 1000 \text{ watts} \times 3600 \text{ seconds} = 3\,600\,000 \text{ joules}$$

TIP A unit is kilowatts multiplied by hours and not kilowatts per hour.

kinetic energy: the *energy* possessed by a moving object.

■ Kinetic energy is proportional to the *mass* of the object and to its speed squared. When a material is heated the molecules have more kinetic energy and so move faster. They therefore make more frequent and more energetic collisions with other molecules. This causes gases to exert greater pressures and chemical reactions to be more rapid. Heat can also cause changes of state from solid to liquid and from liquid to gas by providing enough energy to break molecular bonds.

$$\text{kinetic energy in joules} = \tfrac{1}{2} \text{ mass in kg} \times (\text{speed in m/s})^2$$

■ *e.g.* The speed squared term explains why the braking distance of a car increases very rapidly as its speed increases. At 20 mph (about 9 m/s) the braking distance is 12 m. At twice the speed, 40 mph, the braking distance is 48 m, four times as great. In each case the thinking distance must be added.

Speed squared $(m/s)^2$ is not the same as acceleration (m/s^2).

kinetic theory: a theory used to explain the behaviour of solids, liquids and gases by assuming that they are all made up of small particles that are always in motion.

■ In solids the particles touch and vibrate about a fixed position; in liquids the particles touch but are free to slide over each other; while in gases the particles are separated and are moving randomly.

lattice: the regular, three-dimensional arrangement of particles within a crystal.
■ The particles can be atoms, ions or molecules.

LDR: see *light-dependent resistor*.

leaching: the loss of minerals from soil into groundwater or streams.
■ Soluble minerals in soil dissolve in rainwater and either trickle down into the water table in the rocks below or run-off with the water along the soil surface into local streams. Fertiliser can leach into nearby rivers if it is applied when crops are growing slowly and not taking up the minerals or if it rains shortly after fertiliser is applied. Leached minerals can lead to *eutrophication*.

LED: see *light-emitting diode*.

light: *electromagnetic waves* that can be seen with the eye and can undergo *reflection, refraction* and *diffraction*.
■ White light contains all the colours of the visible *spectrum*. These are red, orange, yellow, green, blue, indigo and violet. Red has the longest wavelength (about 700 nm) and violet the shortest (about 400 nm). On the screen of a colour television tube the correct proportions of red, green and blue light can produce the sensation of white light. You can see these three separate colours if you examine the screen with a magnifying glass.

TIP

You can remember the colours of the spectrum using 'Richard Of York Gave Battle In Vain', or you might prefer 'Real Old Yokels Gorge Beer In Volume'.

light-dependent resistor (LDR): a resistor whose resistance falls when light falls on it and so allows more current to flow.
■ Light-dependent resistors are used in many control systems.
■ *e.g.* An LDR can be used to turn on a light when it gets dark. LDRs are also used as sensors in burglar alarms and to control the motor driving the belt carrying goods at a supermarket checkout.

light-emitting diode (LED): a *diode* that emits light of one wavelength when current flows through it in the conducting direction.
■ The commonest LEDs emit red, green or yellow light.

lightning conductor: a pointed copper rod fixed above the highest point of a building which is connected to earth by a copper conductor.
■ The point attracts lightning to itself rather than the building and the copper conducts the lightning safely to earth.

limestone: a *sedimentary rock* composed mainly of calcium carbonate ($CaCO_3$).
■ Limestone is made from the shells of marine organisms or is precipitated from solution, mostly in the ocean. Various types of limestone are used in building.

limiting factor: a factor that controls how quickly a process can proceed.
■ *e.g.* in *photosynthesis,* the rate at which sugar is made depends on the quantities of carbon dioxide and light available and on the temperature. If there is plenty of carbon dioxide and light but the temperature is low, the rate of photosynthesis is low. If the temperature is raised then photosynthesis goes faster. Similarly, if carbon dioxide is in short supply even though it is warm and there is plenty of light, the rate will be determined by how much carbon dioxide is present.

lipid: a class of molecules that includes fats and oils.
■ Lipids are used for waterproofing, energy storage and making cell membranes. Fat molecules release twice as much energy as carbohydrates and are used as long-term energy stores.

liquid: a state of matter in which the particles touch but are able to move over each other.
■ Liquids are usually runny fluids which occupy a fixed volume but not a fixed shape.

lithosphere: the outer, rigid layer of the Earth containing the *crust* and the plates.

live: an electrical conductor which is at a high voltage relative to *earth.*
■ The live wire in a cable has brown insulation and, in a 13-amp *plug,* is connected to the *fuse.* In a 13-amp socket with the earth at the top, the live socket is on the right.

longitudinal wave: a *wave* transmitted by particles that oscillate in the same direction as the motion of the wave.
■ *Sound waves* and *P waves* are both longitudinal waves. Compare them with *transverse waves.*

loudspeaker: a device that converts electrical oscillations into sound oscillations.
■ The commonest type of loudspeaker has a cone attached to a coil of wire supported in a magnetic field. *Alternating currents* in the wire force the coil in

and out and the cone radiates the sound. Loudspeakers of different sizes are often used together; the smallest radiate the highest frequencies and the largest radiate the lowest frequencies.

lymph: fluid derived from tissue fluid, which drains into lymphatic channels and then empties into the circulatory system.

■Blood loses a large part of the plasma to the tissues as it passes through a *capillary* network. Much of this is returned to the blood, but the rest passes into lymph vessels running through the tissues. Lymph vessels join up to form large ducts that empty lymph back into the bloodstream near the collarbone. At intervals, lymph enters lymph nodes which remove any foreign particles such as microbes. Fat absorbed in the gut passes to lymph vessels called lacteals in the centre of the villi for transport round the body.

lymphocyte: a type of white cell found in the blood.

■Lymphocytes respond to 'foreign' material in the body.

■ *e.g.* B-lymphocytes make *antibodies* that stick to foreign objects such as bacteria and viruses; these help to inactivate them and mark them for destruction. T-lymphocytes activate B-lymphocytes when an infection starts. They also monitor body cells and destroy unusual or infected cells. The human immuno-deficiency virus (HIV) destroys T-lymphocytes so the body cannot respond to infections.

macromolecule: a large, covalent molecule — usually organic.
■ Macromolecules might be biological in origin — such as starch or haemo-globin — or they can be large synthetic *polymers* such as poly(ethene) or poly(phenylethene).

magma: another name for molten rock from the Earth's mantle or crust.
■ When magma solidifies, it forms igneous rocks. When it reaches the surface of the earth it is called lava.

magnet: a piece of steel or ceramic material which has two poles — north-seeking and south-seeking — and which produces a *magnetic field*.
■ Like poles repel each other and unlike poles attract. Either pole will attract a piece of unmagnetised iron, steel, nickel or cobalt.

TIP
The Earth's magnetic pole in northern Canada is a south-seeking pole.

magnetic field: the region near a *magnet* or an electric current where pieces of iron and other magnetic materials will experience forces.
■ Magnetic fields are often represented by lines going from a north-seeking pole to a south-seeking pole or circling round a conductor carrying a current. Strong magnetic fields are needed in *a.c.* and *d.c. generators*.

TIP
A small plotting compass will show the direction of the magnetic field at any point.

magnetic force on a current: a conductor carrying a current in a magnetic field will be forced sideways in a direction that is at right angles to the current and also at right angles to the magnetic field.
■ This is the force that turns electric *motors*.

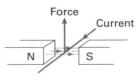

mains electricity: *alternating current* with a *frequency* of 50 *hertz* and a *voltage* of 230 *volts*.

■ Mains electricity is distributed through the *national grid* at 50 Hz but at much higher voltages. The voltage is reduced to 230 V by *transformers*.

malleability: the ability of a substance to be hammered or pressed into different shapes without breaking. Most metals are malleable.

mantle: the zone of molten rock situated in the region of the Earth between the *crust* and the *core*.

■ It amounts to 82% of the Earth's volume and extends from a depth of about 30 km to about 2900 km. The mantle is composed of magnesium, silicon and oxygen, in the form of silicate minerals.

marble: a *metamorphic rock* formed from limestone.

■ In its pure form it is white and consists almost entirely of calcite ($CaCO_3$). Mineral impurities give it various colours and patterns. It is used in building and for statues.

mass: the quantity of matter in a body.

■ More precisely, the mass of a body tells you how much it resists being accelerated by a force. From *Newton's second law*:

$$\text{mass} = \frac{\text{the force applied to the body}}{\text{the acceleration produced}}$$

TIP

It is important to distinguish between mass and *weight* and holding a heavy object at arms length can help you. If you make it oscillate sideways the mass will tell you how difficult it is to do this. The difficulty would be the same on Earth, on the Moon or in outer space, for the mass will be the same in all these places. On the other hand, the weight of the body tells you how difficult it is to support; this would be different in these three places, as the weight varies with the gravitational field strength.

mass flow: a mechanism for the movement of sugars through a plant and, in other organisms, the movement of large quantities of materials in a transport system, as in the circulatory system.

■ The mass-flow hypothesis is used to explain sugar movement in phloem. In the leaves, sugars made in photosynthesis are continuously added to sap in phloem vessels. Water is drawn in by osmosis and this increases pressure in the phloem sieve tubes. Because sugars are removed from sap in the roots for respiration and starch production, there is a pressure gradient through the phloem vessels from leaves to roots and so a mass flow of sugar solution takes place through phloem.

mass number (also called 'nucleon number'): the total number of protons and neutrons within the nucleus of a given element.

■ *e.g.* Carbon has a mass number of 12 (6 protons and 6 neutrons).

master piston: a piston that is driven by a motor to produce a high *pressure* in the liquid in a *hydraulic system*.
■ *e.g.* The brake pedal in a car pushes the master piston. This forces liquid into the slave pistons which operate the brakes.

maternal antibodies: *antibodies* produced by a pregnant woman that pass into a baby either across the placenta or via breast milk.
■ Newborn babies are protected from infections by maternal antibodies while their own immune system matures.

medulla oblongata: a part of the brain that controls many automatic body functions such as breathing and heart rate.
■ These functions often use *reflexes*.
■ *e.g.* A high carbon dioxide concentration in the blood is detected by specialised sensory nerve endings in the arteries near the heart and in the brain itself. Impulses pass to the respiratory centre in the medulla oblongata. This sends an impulse to the muscles involved in breathing; breathing rate increases and carbon dioxide is excreted from the lungs.

meiosis: a specialised form of cell division which produces the cells that become sperm and eggs in animals and the equivalent in pollen and ovules.
■ During the division, the pairs of *homologous chromosomes* become separated, one going into each new cell, so the new cells carry half of the usual number of chromosomes. On fertilisation, each chromosome in the egg has a partner chromosome in the sperm and the normal number of chromosomes is restored in the fertilised egg.

melting point: the temperature at which a substance changes from a solid to a liquid.
■ It is a physical property which can be used to identify a solid. Pure solids of a peculiar substance melt at a fixed temperature; impure solids melt over a range of temperatures.

Mendelian genetics: a pattern of inheritance described by Gregor Mendel (1822–84).
■ Mendel deduced rules that govern the inheritance of genetic features, carried as pairs of factors on a pair of chromosomes. Mendel used the terms 'dominant' to describe a factor that is expressed if an individual inherits it, and 'recessive' for a factor that is not expressed if a dominant form is present. Later on, William Bateson, an English geneticist, coined the word *allele* to describe these dominant and recessive factors. He deduced that only one of a pair of factors (alleles) carried by a parent passes into a sperm or egg. When an egg is fertilised by a sperm, each contributes an allele to make a pair. Mendel is often described as the 'father of genetics', but the term *gene* was not used until 1909.

menstrual cycle: the cycle of hormonal and physical changes that occurs in a woman's body to ripen and release an egg.
- It controls the release of a mature egg and prepares the uterus to support it. Undeveloped eggs (ova) remain in pockets of cells in the ovary until a *hormone* from the brain triggers one into development. This happens at the same time as menstruation (a woman's period). Over the next 10–14 days the egg matures and the ovary makes oestrogen, which thickens the lining of the uterus. The egg is released (ovulation) and the pocket of cells makes progesterone while the egg travels to the uterus. Progesterone also inhibits the brain hormone and so stops another egg developing. Progesterone production ceases if the egg does not implant in the uterus; the brain hormone starts another egg and the uterus lining is lost in menstruation.

metabolism: the life processes within an organism that provide for its needs.
- Metabolism includes the physical and chemical processes taking place within cells to make and degrade substances. It includes processes such as protein synthesis, respiration (which releases energy) and photosynthesis (which produces glucose).

metal: an element that conducts heat and electricity, and exhibits *malleability* and *ductility*.
- Metals occur to the left and centre of the periodic table. Chemically, metals form basic oxides, and in compounds they form cations. Metals can mix to form an alloy — a new substance that combines the most useful properties of its components.

metallic bond: a bond formed within metals.
- The metal donates electrons into a sea of electrons which holds the metal cations together. The sea of electrons is responsible for conduction in metals, and also allows the layers of cations to slide over each other (see *malleability* and *ductility*) without coming apart.

metalloid: an element that has properties of both metals and non-metals.
- *e.g.* Silicon and germanium — they are both semi-conductors, having electrical resistances between those of good conductors and good insulators.

metamorphic rock: rock that has been altered in structure and composition by pressure or heat after its original formation.
- *e.g. Marble*, which was originally formed as chalk or limestone.

meteor: a small object that enters the Earth's atmosphere from interplanetary space.
- Meteors are heated by friction with the air and glow brightly as they enter the Earth's atmosphere and shoot across the sky, so they are often called 'shooting stars'.

m

meteorites: pieces of mineral large enough to reach the Earth's surface from interplanetary space without burning up completely.

meter: an electrical instrument that measures current (an *ammeter*), voltage (a *voltmeter*) or some other quantity. (See also *electricity meter.*)

methane: a colourless, odourless gas formed by the decomposition of plant or animal matter by bacteria.
- Methane (CH_4) is found together with crude oil, and is also one of the main components of *biogas*. It is mainly used as a fuel.

methanol: the simplest of the class of organic compounds called *alcohols*.
- Methanol (CH_3OH) is usually made from coal or natural gas. When pure, it is a colourless, flammable liquid with a pleasant odour, and is highly poisonous.
- Methanol is used as a fuel and as a precursor for other chemicals.

microbe (also called 'microorganism'): any microscopic organism (see *bacterium*, *fungus* and *virus*).
- Some microbes cause disease; others are *decomposers*. Some are used to produce useful products, such as *antibiotics* and *alcohol*.

microphone: a device that converts sound waves into small electrical oscillations which can then be amplified.
- One type of microphone has a coil moving in a magnetic field. It is like a very delicate version of a *loudspeaker*.

micropropagation: a technique used in horticulture where small samples of plant tissue are used to generate hundreds of identical plants.
- A small sample of plant tissue, such as a bud or a section of root, is cut and surface-sterilised. It is placed on sterile agar jelly, containing sucrose, plant hormones and useful growth substances. The cells in the sample multiply and become new shoots and roots. When the plantlets are large enough they are transplanted and grown on in a greenhouse. The plantlets are genetically identical and so form a *clone*.

microwaves: *electromagnetic waves* with a wavelength of about 3 cm.
- Microwaves are some of the shortest radio waves. They can be aimed in narrow beams which are used for radar and for communications between fixed points on Earth or with *satellites* using 'satellite dishes'. They are also absorbed by water molecules and so are used to heat food containing water in microwave ovens. These ovens need interlocking switches and screening to prevent the microwaves from heating the inside of a person's body and causing injury.

mineral: an inorganic element or compound that occurs naturally in the Earth and has a regular arrangement of atoms or ions.
- *e.g.* Quartz (SiO_2).

mitosis: the process of making new cells by cell division.

▥ The mechanism ensures that new cells have a complete copy of inherited information. A cell duplicates its DNA shortly before it divides. During mitosis the DNA within a cell becomes visible as chromosomes. Each *chromosome* is composed of two parts, called *chromatids*, linked together at a junction called the centromere. The chromosomes move to the centre of the cell where they become attached to a structure called the spindle, made of protein fibres. The spindle assists the two chromatids in each chromosome to separate from each other and move to opposite ends of the cell. At the end of mitosis there is a collection of chromatids at each end of the cell, each being half of a chromosome, but carrying the full complement of inherited information.

mixture: two or more substances that have been physically mixed together.

▥ Mixtures do not have a fixed composition. No chemical reactions occur between the components of the mixture, and they can be separated easily by physical means.

▥ *e.g.* Air is a mixture of nitrogen, oxygen, argon, carbon dioxide and other gases.

molar solution: a solution containing 1 mole of substance dissolved in 1 litre ($1\,dm^3$) of solution.

▥ The concentration is known as its molarity and units are in mol/dm^3.

▥ *e.g.* 58.5g of sodium chloride (1 mole) dissolved in $1\,dm^3$ of solution is known as a 1 molar solution, and has a concentration of $1\,mol/dm^3$.

mole: 1 mole of any substance contains *Avogadro's number* (6×10^{23}) of particles of that substance.

▥ It is the same as the formula mass expressed in grams.

▥ *e.g.* Calcium carbonate ($CaCO_3$) has a formula mass of 100. Therefore, 1 mole of calcium carbonate has a mass of 100g and contains 6×10^{23} molecules of calcium carbonate.

molecular mass (also called 'relative molecular mass'): the mass of a molecule compared with $\frac{1}{12}$ of the mass of an atom of carbon-12.

▥ Molecular mass is obtained by adding together the masses of each of the constituent atoms within the molecule.

▥ *e.g.* The molecular mass of sulphuric acid (H_2SO_4) is:

$$(2 \times 1) + 32 + (4 \times 16) = 98$$

molecule: the smallest particle of an element or compound that can exist independently.

▥ A molecule of a compound consists of two or more different atoms bonded together. Molecules vary in size and complexity from the hydrogen molecule (H_2) to the large macromolecules of polymers and proteins. The molecular structure is the order in which the different atoms in the molecule are bonded to each other.

m

moment: the force causing something to turn about a pivot multiplied by the perpendicular distance from the line of force to the pivot.

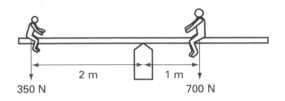

- When something is in equilibrium the sum of the moments of forces tending to move it clockwise equals the sum of the moments tending to turn it anti-clockwise.
- *e.g.* On a seesaw, the heavier person has to sit nearer the centre to make it balance. The clockwise moment, $700\,N \times 1\,m$ = the anticlockwise moment, $350\,N \times 2\,m$.

momentum: the mass in kg × the velocity in m/s of a moving object, measured in kg m/s, symbol p.

- $p = mv$. In any collision or explosion with no external forces, the total momentum is conserved. (See *conservation of momentum*.)
- *e.g.* If a 2 kg trolley moving to the right with a velocity of 3 m/s collides with and sticks to a 6 kg trolley moving to the left at 1 m/s, the trolleys will end up stationary. The total momentum before collision is $(2 \times 3 - 6 \times 1)\,kg\,m/s = 0$.

> **TIP** In such calculations it is important to decide which direction is positive (motion to the right in this example). Velocities in the opposite direction have to be considered negative.

monitoring satellite: a *satellite* that observes as much of the Earth's surface as possible and so is in a polar *orbit*.

- An orbit close to the Earth takes about 90 minutes; higher orbits take longer. As the satellite follows its orbit from pole to pole the Earth rotates beneath it and so the satellite can observe most of the Earth every 12 hours.

monomer: a small organic molecule that can be joined to others to form a larger molecule called a *polymer*.

- Monomers usually contain carbon–carbon double bonds (e.g. ethene polymerises to form poly(ethene)). However, some may join by forming a small molecule in addition to the polymer (condensation polymerisation).

Moon: Earth's largest and only natural *satellite*.

- The *gravitational field strength* on the surface of the Moon is about one sixth that on Earth. So the *weight* of a *mass* on the Moon will be about one sixth of its weight on Earth. The Moon is the main cause of the tides. The water nearest the Moon is in a stronger gravitational field of the Moon than the rest of the Earth and so rises up slightly. On the opposite side of the Earth, the water is in a weaker field and so bulges slightly away from the Moon. Thus, as the Earth rotates, there are high tides at intervals of about 12 hours 25 minutes, but the irregularities in the continents and oceans cause many variations. When the Moon is new or full the Sun's gravitational field is added to the Moon's, causing spring tides — the tides spring up higher. At half Moon, the Sun's field is at right angles to the Moon's and the neap tides are the smallest.

motor: an electrical machine that uses the *magnetic force on a current* to produce rotation and so transfer electrical energy to *kinetic energy*.
- d.c. motors can also be used as *d.c. generators* and so convert kinetic energy to electrical energy.

mutagen: a chemical or other factor that changes the structure of *DNA* molecules.
- Some mutagens react chemically with DNA or physically change the molecule. *Bases* might be changed, sections of DNA deleted or new bases inserted. All mutagens change the sequence of bases along that section of the DNA molecule, and so will affect how that particular gene works. This is *mutation*.
- *e.g.* Ultraviolet light.

mutation: an alteration in the sequence of *bases* along a *DNA* molecule.
- A mutation is caused by a *mutagen*; often it can appear spontaneously and the cause is not known. The changed base sequence in the gene can change the amino acids incorporated into the protein encoded by that gene. This in turn can cause a change in the protein's structure and alter its properties; it might not work as well as the original protein or it might function more effectively. Mutations are one source of genetic variation upon which *natural selection* can operate.
- *e.g.* A change in a single amino acid in the haemoglobin molecule can result in a condition called *sickle-cell anaemia*.

mutualism (also called 'symbiosis'): a close relationship between individuals of two species in which both benefit from the association.
- Each organism gains a benefit from its partner without cost to itself, and usually grows better in the partnership than by itself.
- *e.g.* Nitrogen-fixing bacteria, **Rhizobium**, live within the roots of plants such as peas, beans and clover. The plants benefit from the nitrogen compounds synthesised by the bacteria and are able to grow in impoverished soils. The bacteria benefit from the supply of sugars and protection.

national grid: the network of high-voltage cables that connects large *a.c. generators* to every part of the country.
■ The high voltages give very efficient transmission of electrical energy along *power lines*; *transformers* reduce the voltages to lower and safer values for use in factories and homes.

natural selection (also called 'survival of the fittest')**:** Darwin's idea that the animals and plants that are most suited to their environment (fittest) are most likely to survive, reproduce successfully and pass on their *genes*.
■ Darwin recognised that animals and plants produce far more offspring than can possibly survive, and that small differences between them may be crucial to how well they survive. Those with features that adapt them well to their surroundings will find food, avoid predators and survive climatic stresses better. They will breed more successfully than others, and if their good features are inherited by their offspring these too will survive better. (See *adaptation*.)
■ *e.g.* Dark forms of peppered moths have a greater chance of survival in soot-polluted areas, but light speckled forms are more likely to survive in clean areas. Dark moths are well camouflaged against sooty tree trunks while predatory birds are more likely to see and kill light forms, which are less likely to breed and pass on their light genes. In cleaner areas light forms are favoured.

nebula: a distant cloud of gas and dust, sometimes glowing and sometimes dark. The term can also mean a galaxy or a large cloud of distant stars.

neurone: the major cell type in the nervous system.
■ Neurones are specialised for passing *impulses* from one to another through the body as part of coordination. Impulses from neighbouring neurones enter a neurone through *dendrites* and pass out of the cell via the *axon*. The main cell body is located in the spinal cord or brain but the axon extends to the cell it serves. The axon is surrounded by a fatty myelin sheath which helps to speed up its transmission. The junction between one neurone and the next is called a *synapse*.

neurotransmitter: a chemical that conveys a nervous impulse from one neurone to the next or to an *effector* cell.

■ When an impulse arrives at the end of an *axon*, molecules of neurotransmitter are released into the minute gap, or *synapse*, between neurones. They diffuse across the gap and bind with receptors on the next cell's membrane where they trigger an impulse. The gap is cleared for the next impulse by the destruction of remaining neurotransmitter molecules or the reabsorption of them for reuse.

neutral, chemistry: a solution that is neither acidic nor alkaline — it has a *pH* of 7 because it has equal numbers of H^+ and OH^- ions.

■ To neutralise a solution means to react an acid with a base so as to form a neutral solution.

TIP

Atoms with equal numbers of protons and electrons are also neutral as they have no overall charge.

neutral, electricity: the mains conductor with blue insulation which is not *live* and which is at about the same voltage as *earth*.

■ *e.g.* In a 13-amp *plug* the neutral wire is connected to the small pin that is not connected to the *fuse*.

neutron: one of the three fundamental particles that make up atoms.

■ Neutrons have a relative mass of 1 and have no charge. They are found in the central nucleus of the atom.

neutron star: a small object about 10^9 times as dense as water which results from the collapse of a *supernova*.

■ The massive star collapses under its own gravitational attraction and its *electrons* and *protons* combine to form *neutrons*. It might then become a *black hole*.

newton: the unit of *force*, symbol N.

■ 1 newton is the force that will *accelerate* a *mass* of 1 kg with an acceleration of $1 m/s^2$. The *weight* of an object is the force with which the Earth attracts it and so is measured in newtons. Weighing machines actually measure the force exerted on them but the scale translates this into mass, as a mass of 1 kg has a weight of 10 N on Earth.

TIP

Make sure that you use kilograms for all your masses and newtons for all your weights and forces. A greengrocer might say: 'This bag of carrots weighs 2 kilograms.' Strictly speaking, a physicist should say: 'This bag of carrots weights 20 newtons. As a mass of 1 kilogram has a weight of 10 newtons on the Earth, the bag of carrots has a mass of 2 kilograms.'

Newton's first law: if there are no unbalanced forces on an object it will move with constant velocity or remain at rest.

■ *e.g.* A person standing still on the floor is in *equilibrium* with balanced forces.

n

A parachutist falling with a steady *terminal velocity* is in equilibrium with balanced forces.

Newton's second law: if there is an unbalanced *force* on an object it will have an *acceleration a* given by: $a = F/m$.

■ *e.g.* As the Moon orbits the Earth it is always accelerating.

> TIP
>
> Changing direction at a constant *speed* needs a force and so this is also an acceleration.

Newton's third law: if A exerts a force on B then B exerts an equal and opposite force on A.

■ *e.g.* If the Earth attracts you ***downwards*** with a force of 700 N (your *weight*) then you attract the Earth ***upwards*** with a force of 700 N.

> TIP
>
> Avoid using the neat phrase 'action and reaction are equal and opposite' as it is very easy to get muddled and confuse *equilibrium* with Newton's third law.

nitric acid: a colourless, viscous liquid, which is both a strong acid and also an oxidising agent.

■ Nitric acid (HNO_3) is made by dissolving nitrogen dioxide in water. Salts of nitric acid contain the NO_3^- group and are called nitrates. Nitric acid is used for making fertilisers, explosives, dyes and pharmaceuticals.

nitrogen: a colourless, diatomic gas (N_2).

■ Each nitrogen atom contains five electrons in its outer shell. Nitrogen gas is unreactive due to the high strength of the nitrogen–nitrogen triple bond. 78% of the air is nitrogen. It can be extracted by *fractional distillation* of liquid air. In the presence of a *catalyst*, nitrogen will react with hydrogen, forming ammonia. (See *nitrogen cycle*.)

nitrogen cycle: the movement of nitrogen between the atmosphere, soil and living organisms.

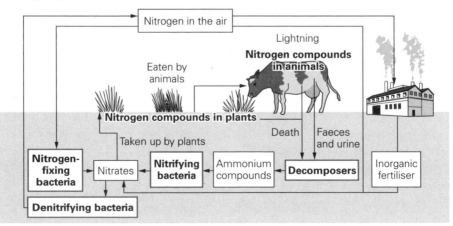

■ Nitrogen in the air is converted to nitrates by lightning, fertilisers and nitrogen-fixing bacteria and washed into the soil. Denitrifying bacteria return it to the air. Plants grow using nitrates from the soil, and are eaten by animals. Excretion and decay return the nitrogen compounds to the soil.

nitrogen fixation: the biological process of using gaseous nitrogen for the synthesis of nitrogen-containing compounds in living cells.

■ Some microorganisms can use nitrogen from the air for synthesising amino acids and other molecules. These substances then become available to other living things in a habitat when the microorganisms die and decompose or when they are eaten. The microbes are responsible for much of the nitrate found in soil.

nitrogenous fertilisers: fertilisers that replenish soluble nitrogen compounds in the soil after they have been used up by plants.

■ Ammonium nitrate is a common source of nitrogen and is made by neutralising nitric acid with ammonia. Nitrogen compounds are needed to promote healthy leaf growth.

nitrogen oxides: Compounds of nitrogen and oxygen, with the general formula NO_x.

■ They are formed by lightning passing through the atmosphere and also in automobile engines. In both cases the high-voltage spark causes the relatively inert nitrogen to combine with oxygen from the air. Oxides of nitrogen are also formed in the Ostwald process for the manufacture of nitric acid, in which ammonia and air are passed over a heated *catalyst* of rhodium and platinum.

■ *e.g.* Nitrogen monoxide (a colourless gas) and nitrogen dioxide (a toxic orange gas).

noble gases: the gases making up group 0 (zero) of the *periodic table* (helium, neon, argon, krypton, xenon and radon).

■ Noble gases all have a full shell of outer electrons and are generally quite unreactive. They are all obtained by the fractional distillation of liquid air. They are used as inert atmospheres and also in discharge tubes where they emit particular colours of light.

non-metal: an element that does not conduct heat and electricity well.

■ Non-metals usually have a low melting point. They occur to the right of the periodic table. Chemically, non-metals form acidic oxides, and in compounds they form anions.

non-renewable energy: *energy resources* that have taken millions of years to develop and so will not be renewed once we have used them.

■ *e.g.* They include *fossil fuels* — coal, oil and gas — and uranium.

NPK (ratio): a way of expressing the proportions of essential plant minerals in a *fertiliser*, using percentage by mass.

n

■ N represents the amount of nitrogen-containing material, such as ammonium or nitrate ions. P signifies the phosphorus-containing material, such as phosphate ions. K signifies the potassium-containing material such as potassium chloride.

■ *e.g.* Different crops require different proportions of NPK. High proportions of N result in lush foliage, which is desirable for leafy crops.

nuclear fuel: *isotopes* of uranium and plutonium that undergo controlled *fission* and so lose *mass* and produce *heat.*

■ The heat produced by the nuclear reactor makes steam. This drives turbines which in turn drive *a.c. generators,* so converting nuclear energy to electrical energy.

nuclear fusion: the combining of light *isotopes* such as deuterium, $_1^2H$, an isotope of hydrogen, to make helium, $_2^4He$. The helium atom has slightly less mass than the two deuterium atoms and the excess mass is converted to heat energy.

■ This process produces heat energy in the Sun and in hydrogen bombs. High-powered research is being carried out into the possibility of using fusion in a controlled manner as it could produce large amounts of energy with little radioactive waste, but there are big problems in containing the reaction at the extremely high temperatures needed.

nuclear model of the atom: see *Rutherford model of the atom.*

nucleic acid: One of a number of very large polymer molecules found in cells which are involved in storing and using inherited information.

■ There are two main types of nucleic acid. *DNA* encodes inherited information. It is located in chromosomes in the nucleus of cells. RNA is found in both the nucleus and in the cytoplasm. RNA is used in the cell processes that carry out the instructions for making proteins encoded in DNA.

nucleon: a particle in the nucleus of an atom — either a *proton* or a *neutron.*

nucleon number: see *mass number.*

nucleus of an atom: the central part of an *atom,* made up of *protons* and *neutrons* and containing almost all the mass of the atom.

■ A number of electrons, equal to the number of protons, circulate around the nucleus in shells, or orbitals. Hydrogen has no neutrons in its nucleus.

nucleus of a cell: the structure that contains genetic material as *DNA* in *chromosomes.*

■ It plays a large part in controlling the activities of the cell, because DNA controls *protein synthesis.* The nucleus is surrounded by membranes which are quite tough, yet they break down when *cell division* occurs to release the chromosomes.

ohm: the unit of *resistance*, Ω.
■ A resistance of 1 ohm has a *potential difference* (or *voltage*) of 1 volt across it when 1 *ampere* flows through it.

Ohm's law: the *potential difference* across a conductor at a constant temperature is proportional to the *current* flowing through it.
■ The ratio of potential difference (*V*)/current flowing (*I*) is called the *resistance* of the conductor and is measured in *ohms*. Thus *V*/*I* = *R*.

onion-skin weathering: see *exfoliation*.

open: the state of *switch* or *relay* contacts when they are not connected.
■ See also *closed*.

optical fibre: a fine fibre of glass which transmits light along its length by *total internal reflection*.
■ Rapid variations of the intensity of the light allow large amounts of data to be transmitted along the fibre much more efficiently than electrically along a copper wire. Optical fibres are being used instead of copper cables for transmitting television pictures, telephone messages and data signals. Bundles of fibres are used to make a flexible 'viewing tube' which can see around corners, as in an *endoscope*.

orbit: the path of a *planet, satellite* or *comet* around a larger attracting mass.
■ Under gravitational attraction these orbits are *ellipses.*

ore: a rock that contains a mineral from which an element can be economically extracted.
■ *e.g. Bauxite*, which contains both aluminium and iron oxides, is the ore of aluminium as it is relatively inexpensive to remove the oxides of iron.

organic: a compound that contains carbon–carbon covalent bonds.
■ There are more than 3 million organic compounds. This large number arises from the ability of carbon to bond to itself many times to form long chains and rings.

O

osmosis: the movement of water molecules across a *partially permeable membrane.*

■ Water molecules move from a dilute solution (where there are few dissolved molecules and lots of water molecules) into a more concentrated solution (more dissolved molecules, fewer water molecules) through a cell membrane. In theory, an animal cell would burst, but the concentration of blood is maintained within limits to prevent this happening. Plant cells in water do not burst because of the restraining cell wall.

■ *e.g.* A piece of dried fruit (not much water) placed in a bowl of tap water (lots of water molecules) swells up as water molecules move into the fruit along the concentration gradient. Swelling ceases when the plant cells are *turgid.*

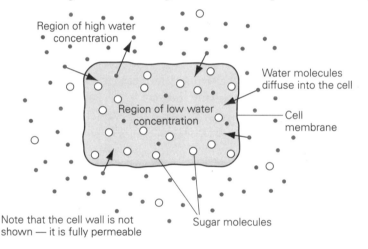

Region of high water concentration

Water molecules diffuse into the cell

Region of low water concentration

Cell membrane

Note that the cell wall is not shown — it is fully permeable

Sugar molecules

TIP

Water molecules move randomly in both directions across the cell membrane, but more move into the cell shown above than out because there are more outside to move in, than there are inside to move out.

oxidation: the addition of oxygen to an element or compound during the course of a reaction. It is also defined as the loss of electrons from an element or compound during the course of a reaction.

■ *e.g.* In the following equation:

$$2\,Mg + O_2 \longrightarrow 2\,MgO$$

the magnesium has been oxidised, and oxygen is the oxidising agent. In this equation:

$$2\,FeCl_2 + Cl_2 \longrightarrow 2\,FeCl_3$$

the $FeCl_2$ has been oxidised (because the iron loses an electron in going from $FeCl_2$ to $FeCl_3$), and chlorine is the oxidising agent.

oxygen: a colourless, diatomic gas (O_2).

■ Each oxygen atom contains six electrons in its outermost shell. 21% of the air is oxygen and it can be extracted by fractional *distillation.* Oxygen is very reactive and supports combustion. It is used for respiration. Industrially, it is used in steel making, welding and breathing apparatus.

oxygen debt: the oxygen needed to remove lactic acid in muscles after intense activity.

■ During intense activity, such as sprinting, glucose is not fully broken down to carbon dioxide in *respiration* because there is not enough oxygen available in muscle cells. Instead, some energy is released by a partial breakdown to lactic acid, which accumulates. Lactic acid can have harmful effects and is metabolised to carbon dioxide as soon as oxygen becomes available at the end of the exertion.

ozone: an *allotrope* of oxygen, with the formula O_3.

■ It is made naturally in the upper atmosphere by the action of the Sun's radiation on oxygen. As such, it forms a very diffuse layer (the ozone layer), and this prevents harmful ultraviolet light from reaching the surface of the Earth. The ozone layer can be destroyed by chemicals released by man, such as chloro-fluorocarbons (CFCs). Ozone is also formed whenever a high-voltage spark passes through oxygen. Ozone is one component of photochemical smog, which forms from *nitrogen oxides* in car exhaust gases on bright sunny days. It is a form of air *pollution*, irritating people's eyes and causing damage to chlorophyll in the leaves of plants, so that their growth is affected.

TIP

Remember, ozone high up in the atmosphere is good; ozone low down is bad! Also, do not confuse the damage to the ozone layer with the *greenhouse effect*.

palisade layer: a layer of cells just under the upper surface of a leaf.

■ The palisade layer, also called palisade mesophyll, is responsible for most *photosynthesis* in a leaf. The transparent epidermal cells and cuticle let light through to the palisade cells. Palisade cells are packed with *chloroplasts* and their long, thin shape enables them to harvest most of the usable light. The layer of cells beneath has large air spaces that act as a reservoir of gases and allow free diffusion of gases to and from the palisade mesophyll cells for photosynthesis.

Pangaea: the name given to the large continental land mass that existed on Earth between 200 and 300 million years ago.

■ Over millions of years Pangaea split up and continental drift moved the continents to their present positions.

paper chromatography: a process used to separate mixtures of coloured liquids.

■ The mixture is placed on special paper and a suitable solvent allowed to flow over it. Some parts of the mixture are carried along by the solvent while other parts are absorbed by the paper. The mixture is separated into separate bands, each band corresponding to one component of the mixture.

parallel circuit: a circuit in which the current divides between two or more components in parallel.

■ The total current before the division equals the sum of all the currents in the components. The component with the highest resistance carries the smallest current. There is the same *potential difference* across every component in parallel.

TIP

Voltmeters should be connected in parallel with a component.

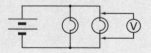

partial reflection: When a wave crosses a boundary between two transparent media, some of the wave is reflected and some is refracted. (See *reflection* and *refraction*.)

p

■ *e.g.* When light meets a boundary between air and glass in either direction, most of the light crosses the boundary but a small amount is reflected. This is why when it is dark outside, you can use a window as a mirror.

partially permeable membrane: a membrane that allows small molecules, but not larger molecules, to pass through.
■ *e.g.* The cell membrane acts as a partially permeable membrane. It does not allow large molecules such as proteins to pass through, but small molecules such as oxygen and water can pass. The membrane can exert some control over what passes through because some molecules of similar sizes can cross a membrane while others are blocked. Visking tubing and dialysis membranes are artificial partially permeable membranes.

pascal: the unit of *pressure*, symbol Pa.
■ 1 pascal is a pressure of 1 *newton* per square metre.
■ *e.g.* Atmospheric pressure is about 100 000 Pa, but it varies with the weather.

p.d.: see *potential difference.*

periodic table: an arrangement of all the known elements, so that their properties occur in a regular manner.
■ The elements are arranged in order of increasing atomic number. The table enables predictions to be made about their behaviour. Vertical columns are called groups, numbered 1–7 and 0; this reflects the number of electrons in the outermost shell. Reactivity increases down the group for metals and up the group for non-metals. Horizontal rows are called periods. A large block of elements, between groups 2 and 3, contains the transition elements, which are characterised by displaying more than one *valency*.

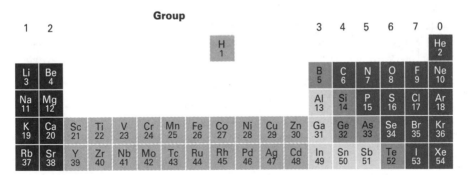

peristalsis: the muscular action in the walls of a tube, such as the gut, which squeezes its contents along.
■ Peristalsis is brought about by the action of layers of muscles. In swallowing, circular muscles behind a pellet of chewed food contract and narrow the tube. This forces the food along the tube where further circular muscle fibres contract to continue the smooth passage along the gut.

p

permanent hardness: a form of hardness in water caused by magnesium and calcium carbonates and sulphates.

■Hard water forms a scum with soap. It cannot be removed by boiling (unlike *temporary hardness*).

pesticide: a substance that kills organisms that have adverse effects on crops, livestock or other human activity. Many pesticides kill species other than the target pest and have to be used with care.

■Insects, such as aphids that eat crops or disease-carrying mosquitoes, are killed by insecticides. Herbicides kill weeds that would compete with growing crops. Fungicides kill moulds growing on crops and stored produce.

petroleum: see *crude oil*.

pH: a measure of the proportion of H^+ ions in aqueous solution compared with OH^- ions that might be present.

■When there are equal numbers of each ion, the pH is 7 and said to be neutral. When there are more H^+ ions present the pH is less than 7 and the solution is acidic. When there are more OH^- ions present the pH is greater than 7 and the solution is alkaline.

TIP

pH = $-\log[H^+]$, where $[H^+]$ is the concentration of H^+ ions.

phenotypic variation: marked differences between individuals sharing the same, or very similar, genes. It is caused by differences between the individuals' environments.

■ *e.g.* Identical twins can be very different, for example if one has suffered ill health or poor nutrition. Plants that are part of a *clone* will vary, depending on how much water, light and nutrients they receive. Even on the same plant there can be variation. Ivy plants can have differently shaped leaves. In the shade at the base of a hedge, an ivy plant has large, broad, dark-green leaves. At the top of the hedge, where they grow in full light, the ivy leaves are small, more pointed and light green.

phloem: specialised transporting cells in plants that carry sugars from leaves and storage tissues to other parts of the plant.

■Phloem cells form the outer layer of cells in *vascular bundles* in stems and leaf stalks.

photosynthesis: the process by which plants make food.

■In photosynthesis, plants trap light and use the energy to convert carbon dioxide and water into glucose. Oxygen is released as a waste product. The process can be summarised in the equation below:

$$6CO_2 + 6H_2O \xrightarrow[\text{Chlorophyll}]{\text{Light}} C_6H_{12}O_6 + 6O_2$$

p

■ *e.g.* Glucose made in photosynthesis can be used in respiration, stored as starch, or converted into amino acids, cellulose, fats and other molecules.

phototropism: a plant's growth response to the direction of light.
■ The green parts of a plant above ground show positive phototropism, that is, they bend in the direction of strongest light intensity. This is the result of larger amounts of *auxin* on the shadier sides of a shoot, causing it to grow more than the sunny side.

physical change: a change that can be easily reversed and which does not alter the chemical properties of a substance.
■ Melting, boiling and sublimation are examples of physical changes.

pipette: a calibrated glass tube used to deliver fixed volumes of liquid very accurately.
■ The liquid is sucked up to the calibration mark and then the required volume is allowed to run out.

placenta: a structure found in mammals which exchanges materials between the blood of a fetus and the blood of its mother.
■ The placenta is formed from tissues of the *embryo* and its mother. It acts as lung, intestine and kidney for the fetus.

TIP

The blood of the fetus and the blood of the mother do not mix. They pass on either side of an *exchange surface*.

planet: a large object in *orbit* around the Sun or some other star.
■ In our solar system, the planets (in order from the closest to the furthest from the Sun) are: Mercury, Venus, Earth, Mars, Jupiter, Saturn, Uranus, Neptune and Pluto.

plankton: microscopic organisms living in the surface layers of ponds, lakes, seas and oceans.
■ The organisms include small invertebrates, fish fry and other aquatic larvae, single-celled algae and diatoms. The algae are *producers* in aquatic food chains. Many larger organisms feed on plankton.

plasma: the liquid part of the blood.
■ Plasma is about 55% of blood by volume and carries dissolved nutrients and waste. It also carries proteins, including *blood clotting* factors, *antibodies*, *hormones* and *proteins*, to help keep the blood pH constant.

plasmolysis: the process in which a plant cell loses water by *osmosis* and the cytoplasm shrinks.
■ This occurs when the plant cell is placed in a solution that contains a higher concentration of solutes than is present inside the cell. Eventually, the living

p

contents of the cell shrink so much that they pull away from the cell wall. This is uncommon in most natural situations.

plate tectonics: the theory that the outermost layer of the Earth, the crust and the upper part of the mantle, is made up of a number of separate plates (seven large plates and a number of small plates).
■ These plates move slowly about the surface, carried by convection currents deep within the Earth. The movement of plates and their interactions are responsible for mountain formation, volcanoes and earthquakes.

plug: a connector that joins two pieces of electrical equipment.
■ A 13-amp plug contains a *fuse* between the *live* pin and its cable. The *earth* pin is the largest of the three.

TIP You must connect the correct cable to each pin. Remember — daffodils grow in **earth** and are green and yellow. **Live** used to be red for danger, but now it has faded to brown. Blue sky is **neutral** and doesn't hurt anyone.

plum-pudding model: an early model of the *atom* which suggested that it was solid with *electrons* embedded in it.
■ *Rutherford's* experiments with alpha particles and gold foil showed that the atom is mostly empty space. The experiments formed the basis of the *Rutherford model of the atom* and did not support the plum-pudding model.

pollution: the introduction by people into the environment of substances or energy liable to cause hazards to human health, harm to living resources and *ecosystems* or damage to structures.
■ *e.g.* There are four major types of pollution: air (e.g. car exhaust gases), water (e.g. fertiliser run-off), land (e.g. litter) and noise (e.g. aircraft).

poly(chloroethene) (also called 'polyvinylchloride' or 'PVC'): the *polymer* made by polymerising chloroethene.
■ Poly(chloroethene) is often used as an electrical insulator for cables and for making pipes and other rigid objects.

poly(ethene) (also called 'polythene'): the polymer made by *polymerising* ethene.
■ It is a thermoplastic. Low-density poly(ethene), which has many branches to the polymer chain, is soft and flexible, while high-density poly(ethene) has few branches and is more rigid as the polymer chains can lie closer together.

polymer: a long-chain organic molecule made by joining many small molecules (*monomers*) together.
■ Polymers occur naturally, or they may be man-made.
■ *e.g.* Proteins and starch occur naturally, while *poly(chloroethene)*, $(C_2H_3Cl)_n$, and *poly(ethene)*, $(C_2H_4)_n$, are the commonest man-made polymers.

polymerisation: the process of joining monomers together to make polymers.

p

■Often a *catalyst* is used to speed up the polymerisation process.

polysaccharide: a carbohydrate polymer usually used for storage or cell structure.
■ These polymers are made of repeating sugar units and are so large that they are insoluble.
■ *e.g.* Cellulose, starch, glycogen and agar.

poly(tetrafluoroethene): see *Teflon*.

polythene: see *poly(ethene)*.

polyvinylchloride: see *poly(chloroethene)*.

population: a group of individuals of the same species occupying a particular habitat at a particular time.
■ *e.g.* oak trees in a wood, salmon in a river, pupils in a school.

potassium-40: a radioactive *isotope* of potassium with a *half-life* of 1.3×10^9 years, accounting for 1 part in 1000 of natural potassium.
■ The ratio of this isotope to its decay product argon is used to date *igneous rocks*.

potential difference (p.d.): the *voltage* across a *resistor* or other component when a current flows through it and *electrical energy* is being converted into some other form. (See *voltage*.)
■ The electrical energy is converted into:
  ● *heat* in a resistor
  ● *kinetic energy* and heat in a *motor*
  ● *light* and heat in a lamp
  ● chemical energy and heat in *electrolysis*
  ● sound and heat in a *loudspeaker* or buzzer

TIP

The potential differences across components in a *series circuit* add up to the total potential difference across the whole circuit. Components in a *parallel circuit* all have the same potential difference across them.

potential divider (also called 'potentiometer'): a circuit that uses a *variable resistor* with three connections to provide voltages from zero up to the maximum voltage across the resistor.
■ Potential dividers can also be made with one fixed resistor and one variable resistor; this could be a thermistor or *light-dependent resistor*.

potential energy: mechanical energy stored in a static form either as *elastic potential energy* or as *gravitational potential energy*.

potometer: a piece of apparatus for measuring the uptake and loss of water from a plant due to transpiration.

power: the rate of transferring *energy*, symbol P.

p

■ Power in *watts* = energy in *joules*/time in seconds. 1 watt is a rate of energy transfer of 1 *joule* per second. A larger unit is the kilowatt. The old unit of the horsepower is sometimes used and is equal to 746 watts.

■ e.g. The power needed to raise a *weight* of 20 newtons through a height of 7 metres in 4 seconds is $20\,N \times 7\,m/4\,s = 35\,W$.

> In electricity it is often convenient to calculate power as current multiplied by voltage, $P = I\,V$.

power line: a high-voltage line that transmits large amounts of electrical *power* using relatively small *currents*.

■ By using high voltages the losses in the *resistance* of the cables are much reduced and thinner cables can be used.

■ e.g. The *national grid* uses voltages of 400 000, 275 000, 132 000, 33 000 and 11 000 volts.

precipitate: an insoluble product that occurs when two solutions are mixed.

■ e.g. When solutions of chloride ions and silver ions are mixed, an insoluble precipitate of silver chloride is formed.

pressure: the force divided by the area on which it is acting, symbol *p*.

■ Pressure is measured in *pascals* (Pa). 1 pascal is a pressure of 1 newton per square metre, and is a relatively small pressure. The pressure in liquids and in the atmosphere increases with depth.

■ e.g. At ground level, atmospheric pressure is about 100 000 Pa which is also called 1 bar. This is also the pressure produced by water 10 metres deep. A *barometer* filled with mercury has a column 760 mm high when registering 'Standard Atmospheric Pressure' whereas one filled with water would need to be about 10 metres tall.

prism: a triangular block of glass that can be used to split white *light* into the colours of the *electromagnetic spectrum*.

■ Prisms with angles of 45°, 45° and 90° use *total internal reflection* to reflect light in some binoculars and periscopes.

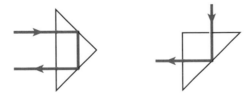

producer: an organism that makes food at the start of a food chain.

■ Plants are producers because they use light to convert carbon dioxide into glucose in the process of *photosynthesis*. The energy fixed in this way is then available to other organisms that eat the plants.

propene: a colourless gas with the formula C_3H_6.
■ Propene contains one carbon–carbon *double bond*. It is made by *cracking* crude oil. It is commonly used for making the polymer polypropene.

protein: a major constituent of organisms, made of long chains of *amino acids*.
■ There are many proteins, each with its own unique structure and function. Examples include *enzymes*, some *hormones* and *antibodies*. Some proteins are contractile (in muscle); others are structural, as in bone, skin, nails and hair. *Mutation* affects *DNA* structure, which in turn affects structure and function, as happens in *inherited disorders*.

proton: one of the three fundamental particles that make up atoms.
■ Protons have a relative mass of 1 and have a positive charge. They are found in the central nucleus of the atom. Different elements have different numbers of protons.

proton number: see *atomic number*.

pumped storage: a system for storing electrical energy by using the *potential energy* of water in one lake that is higher than another lake.
■ When there is a sudden demand for electric power the water from the top lake is released and as it falls to the bottom lake through large pipes it gains *kinetic energy* and drives turbines and *generators*. When there is spare electric power at night the water is pumped back to the top lake. This is a complicated but practical way of storing electrical energy.
■ *e.g.* There are pumped storage power stations at Foyers in north Scotland and at Dinorwig and Ffestiniog in north Wales.

PVC: see *polychloroethene*.

P wave: a *longitudinal wave*, caused by an earthquake, that travels through the *mantle* and the *core* of the Earth.
■ Longitudinal waves can travel through liquids as well as solids and so travel through all parts of the Earth, whereas *S waves* travel only through solids.

pyramid of biomass: a diagrammatic way of representing the quantity of organisms per unit area in a food chain.
■ The *biomass* of plants in a given area forms the first step of the pyramid, the biomass of herbivores feeding on these plants in the area forms the second step, and so on. A pyramid of biomass allows habitats involving a few large organisms, for example trees, to be compared with habitats supported by small, numerous organisms such as algae.

TIP
Pyramids of biomass are always broad-based, unlike pyramids of number which may have a single, large plant at the base, or thousands of tiny parasites at the top.

quadrat: a piece of apparatus used to estimate the populations of plants and static animals.

■ The quadrat is a square frame of known area, subdivided into smaller squares. It is placed at the *sampling* site and the number of individuals in the quadrat counted or the area they cover assessed. Several samples are counted and an average found to give a more accurate estimate.

quartz: A crystalline form of silicon dioxide (SiO_2) in which all the atoms are regularly arranged.

■ Sand is impure quartz with iron impurities.

quartz-iodine lamp: a compact lamp with a tungsten filament running at a higher temperature than in a normal lamp. The bulb is made of quartz to withstand the high temperature and contains iodine to reduce the evaporation of the filament.

■ The lamp is more efficient than a normal filament lamp, giving more light per joule of energy on account of the higher temperature.

quasar: a quasi-stellar object with a high *red shift*.

■ The high red shift suggests that quasars are moving away from us extremely fast and are the most distant luminous objects in the universe. This means that they must be extremely bright.

quicklime: another name for calcium oxide (CaO).

■ Quicklime is formed by heating calcium carbonate strongly. It is used for neutralising acidity in water and in the soil.

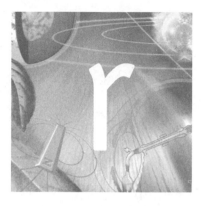

radiation, heat: the emission of *electromagnetic waves* from a hot source.

■ Cool sources radiate in the *infrared*. At higher temperatures, the radiation extends into the red end of the visible *electromagnetic spectrum* until, at the Sun's temperature, all colours are radiated and white light is emitted. Unless electromagnetic waves are focused into a beam, their intensity falls off with distance from the source. (See also *infrared*.)

radiation, nuclear: the emission of *alpha particles, beta particles* and *gamma rays* from a source of *radioactivity*.

radioactivity: the spontaneous breakdown of the nucleus of an atom, releasing small particles or electromagnetic radiation.

■ A new element is usually formed. The particles emitted can be *alpha particles* (2 protons and 2 neutrons) or *beta particles* (fast-moving electrons).

TIP

The radiation decreases rapidly if the *isotope* has a short *half-life*, or slowly if it has a long half-life.

radiocarbon dating: see *carbon dating*.

radioisotope: an *isotope* of an element that is radioactive.

■ *e.g.* Carbon-14 is an isotope of carbon that forms a very small percentage of carbon dioxide in the air. It has a *half-life* of 5570 years and is used for dating any dead material that contains carbon incorporated from the air while it was alive.

radionuclide: see *radioisotope*.

radio waves: *electromagnetic waves* longer than 1 mm.

■ Waves shorter than 10 cm can be focused into a beam, but longer waves are generally broadcast in all directions. The longest waves used have *wavelengths* of about 3000 m.

rate of reaction: the speed at which a reaction occurs.

■ The rate of reaction is measured by investigating the rate at which reactants are used up, or the rate at which products are formed. Reactions have a faster rate if reactants are made more concentrated, if they have a larger surface area, if the temperature is raised or if a *catalyst* is used.

raw material: a substance obtained from a natural resource that can be used to make other substances.
- *e.g.* Coke, limestone and iron ore are the raw materials used in the production of iron.

reactivity series: an arrangement of metallic elements with the most reactive first and the least reactive last.
- More reactive metals will displace less reactive metals from a solution of their ions (see *displacement*). The more reactive a metal the more stable are its compounds, and the harder it is to extract from its ore.

receptor: a nerve cell that is sensitive to a *stimulus* from the environment and which generates a nervous impulse.
- Receptors allow animals to sense changes in the external environment and within the body. Each type detects one sort of stimulus only. The impulse passes along a sensory *neurone* to the *central nervous system* where a response is coordinated.
- *e.g.* The skin houses receptors for pain, touch, pressure, heat and cold. Some receptors are located within specialised organs such as the eye or ear. Internal receptors include those for muscle tension and carbon dioxide concentration in the blood.

recessive allele: a version of a gene that is not expressed in the presence of a *dominant allele* (gene).
- Recessive alleles are only expressed when an individual has inherited two copies, one from each parent.
- *e.g.* In the case of height in pea plants, a dwarf pea plant would be a *homozygote*, with two recessive alleles. In the *heterozygote*, the dominant allele would be expressed (not the recessive allele) and the plant would be tall.

recycling: the process whereby used substances are used as a source of raw materials.
- Paper, glass and plastics can all be recycled. Recycling usually requires less energy than was originally used to make the substance. It slows down the loss of non-renewable resources and helps to reduce pollution.
- *e.g. Aluminium* is frequently recycled because of its value and its properties that allow it to be melted down and re-formed without loss of quality (unlike paper and glass, which deteriorate when recycled).

red blood cell: the most abundant type of cell in the blood. Red blood cells are small, biconcave discs packed with haemoglobin, and specialised for carrying oxygen.

■ They have no nucleus, once fully developed, and a short life span (around 3 months).

red giant: the stage in a star's life when it expands and cools after the main, stable, part of its life.
■ A large red giant will become a *supernova* and a small one will become a *white dwarf*.
■ *e.g.* The Sun will become a red giant after its present stable state.

redox: a reaction in which one reactant undergoes *reduction* and the other reactant undergoes *oxidation* simultaneously.
■ *e.g.* Hydrogen reduces lead(II) oxide to lead while it is itself oxidised to water:
$$H_2 + PbO \longrightarrow Pb + H_2O$$

red shift: the shift towards the red end of the *electromagnetic spectrum* of the light from a *star* or *galaxy* that is moving away from us at a high speed.
■ The faster the object is moving away, the greater the red shift. (See *Doppler effect.*)

reduction: the removal of oxygen from a compound during the course of a reaction. It is also defined as the gaining of electrons by an element or compound during the course of a reaction.
■ *e.g.* In the following equation:
$$PbO + H_2 \longrightarrow Pb + H_2O$$
the lead oxide has been reduced, and hydrogen is the reducing agent. In this equation:
$$2\,FeCl_2 + Cl_2 \longrightarrow 2\,FeCl_3$$
the Cl_2 has been reduced (because it gains an electron in going from Cl_2 to Cl^-), and iron(II) chloride is the reducing agent.

reed switch: a *switch* made of two thin reeds of metal which is *closed* when a magnet is brought near to it.
■ The switch can also be made to close when it is inside a coil carrying a current. It is then known as a reed relay.

reflection: a *wave* or a ray of *light* is reflected when it meets a boundary between two media and then returns to the first medium. Both the ray of light and its reflection make the same angles with the reflecting surface.

These angles are the same

■ At a transparent surface there is partial reflection unless the ray is meeting a less-dense medium, and the angle between the ray and the surface is small, when there can be *total internal reflection*. At an opaque, polished boundary there is total reflection.

reflex: an automatic pattern of nervous activity and behaviour generated as a result of a stimulus.

■ Reflexes use a chain of *neurones* in a reflex arc. A *stimulus* is perceived by a *receptor* — an impulse passes along a sensory neurone to the central nervous system. A relay neurone passes the impulse to a motor neurone which conveys the impulse to an *effector* such as a muscle. When the impulse reaches the effector, action takes place. Most reflexes are protective and allow action to be taken to protect the body while the brain is still coordinating information about the cause of the stimulus and longer-term responses.

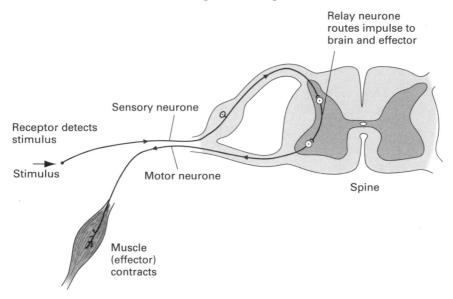

Relay neurone routes impulse to brain and effector

Sensory neurone

Receptor detects stimulus

Stimulus

Motor neurone

Spine

Muscle (effector) contracts

refraction: the change in the direction of a *wave* or a ray of *light* as it crosses a boundary between two different media.

■ When a ray of light goes from air to water it bends so that it travels closer to the normal (the line perpendicular to the surface). When it goes from water to air it bends away from the normal, unless it suffers *total internal reflection*.

■ *e.g.* White light passing through a *prism* is refracted twice and comes out in a new direction. At the same time the different colours of the *electromagnetic spectrum* are separated.

relative formula mass: see *formula mass*.

relative molecular mass: see *molecular mass*.

relay: a *switch* operated by an electric current.

■ A relay can have one or more sets of contacts which can be normally *open* (N.O.) or normally *closed* (N.C.).

■ *e.g.* In a car, the starter switch sends a small current through a relay which then switches on a much larger current to start the car.

renewable energy: resources of energy that will continue to be available or can be replaced as they are used.
- *e.g.* These include solar power, *hydroelectric power* from falling water and power from the wind and from *waves* at sea. Solar power comes directly from the Sun's heat. *Tidal power* comes mainly from the Moon's motion. Wood and other biomass fuels, including manure and biogas, store energy from the Sun and can be replaced in a few years.

resistance: a resistance to the flow of electricity in a *conductor* and the consequent transformation of *electrical energy* to *heat*.
- The resistance of a conductor is measured in *ohms* and is given by the *potential difference* (*voltage*) across the conductor divided by the *current* flowing through it in *amperes*.
- *e.g.* If a *resistor* passes a current of 3 amps when the potential difference across it is 12 volts, then its resistance is $R = 12\,V/3\,A = 4\,\Omega$.

The three formulae connecting R, V and I are:

$$R = V/I$$
$$I = V/R$$
$$V = I\,R$$

where R is resistance, V is potential difference and I is current. The triangle diagram can help you to get these right. Covering the letter you want (for example I) leaves the answer (V/R).

resistor: an electrical component that is designed to have a certain *resistance* to the flow of *current*.
- The resistance is marked on the resistor, often with colours, and its size indicates the *power* that it can safely dissipate. Some made of carbon compounds can be very small and have *resistances* as high as millions of ohms. Others made with coils of fine resistance wire are larger, but can dissipate more power. (See also *variable resistor.*) When resistors are connected in a *series circuit*, the total resistance is equal to the sum of the separate resistances. When two resistors are connected in *parallel*, the equivalent resistance is equal to their product divided by their sum:

$$R = R_1R_2/(R_1 + R_2)$$

When three or more resistors are connected in parallel you need the formula
$$1/R = 1/R_1 + 1/R_2 + 1/R_3$$

respiration: the process of releasing energy from food.

■ Every cell carries out respiration to obtain the energy it needs for its activity. Most cells use aerobic respiration, which produces large amounts of energy. It uses oxygen and releases carbon dioxide. The process can be summarised by the equation

$$C_6H_{12}O_6 + 6O_2 \longrightarrow 6CO_2 + 6H_2O + \text{Energy}$$

Some cells, such as muscle cells and yeast, can use *anaerobic respiration* when there is a shortage of oxygen. This produces less energy but does not need oxygen.

> **TIP** Although plants make energy-containing compounds during photosynthesis, don't forget that they have to respire these compounds to obtain the energy for normal life processes.

restriction enzyme: an enzyme that can cut DNA molecules into smaller fragments.
■ Restriction enzymes are used to snip genes from DNA for transfer into another cell in *genetic modification* processes.

reversible reaction: a reaction in which the products of a reaction recombine to form the reactants.
■ It is indicated in equations by the use of a double-headed arrow.
■ *e.g.* During the manufacture of ammonia, nitrogen and hydrogen combine to give ammonia molecules. At the same time the ammonia breaks down to re-form nitrogen and hydrogen:

$$N_2 + 3H_2 \rightleftharpoons 2NH_3$$

rheostat: a *variable resistor* with two connections, used to vary the current in a circuit.
■ A rheostat is connected in a *series circuit* with a component such as a lamp. It will vary the brightness of the lamp but it cannot reduce the current to zero.

rock cycle: the changing of one type of rock into another — a process that can take many millions of years.
■ *Igneous rock* is weathered and converted to *sedimentary rock*. Heat and pressure turn this into *metamorphic rock*. Eventually this is returned deep into the Earth where it melts to be once again extruded as igneous rock.

ruminant: one of a group of animals with a complex extension to the gut including a rumen.
■ Few organisms produce the *enzymes* needed to digest the *cellulose* in plant cell walls. Decomposers such as *fungi* and *bacteria* can, and many animals rely on these microorganisms living in their guts. The rumen houses microbes that can digest cellulose. Ruminants such as cows graze and swallow vegetation into the rumen for cellulose digestion before the food enters the true gut. Methane gas produced by these organisms contributes to the greenhouse effect.

rust: the common name for hydrated iron(III) oxide, $Fe_2O_3.xH_2O$.

■ Rust is formed whenever oxygen and water attack iron. It is loosely held onto the surface of the iron and so rusting is able to continue underneath. Prevention of rusting involves stopping either one or both of these substances from coming into contact with the iron.

Rutherford model of the atom (also called 'nuclear model of the atom'): the model that superseded the *plum-pudding model*. It says that the *atom* has a small positive nucleus at the centre, containing *protons* and *neutrons* with *electrons* in orbit around it.

■ The British physicist Ernest Rutherford fired *alpha particles* at gold foil and found that most of them went straight through. The deflections of the other particles supported the idea that atoms had very small, positively charged *nuclei*.

salt: a compound formed by the combination of an acid with a base.
■ Salts contain ions.
■ *e.g.* Copper(II) sulphate ($CuSO_4$) and sodium nitrate ($NaNO_3$).

TIP The word salt is often used as the common name for sodium chloride (NaCl).

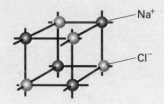

sampling: a technique for the systematic and accurate estimation of how much of something is present.
■ It is very hard to count exactly how many bluebell plants there are in a wood, or measure how heavy flies are because of the large numbers and the variation in the *populations*. Several small samples are measured, taken randomly to compensate for variation. The figures are used to make an estimate of the population as a whole.
■ *e.g.* A *quadrat* is used to estimate the number of daisies in a field. Several sites in the field are selected randomly and the quadrat used to count the daisy plants in each sample. An average of the sites is used to calculate the number per m^2 in the field.

satellite: a small object in space that is in *orbit* around a much larger object under the attraction of *gravity*.
■ Natural satellites around *planets* are called moons. The many artificial satellites in orbit around the Earth are mostly *communications satellites* or *monitoring satellites*.

TIP The further a satellite is from the Earth the more slowly it travels and the longer is the time it takes to complete an orbit.

saturated compound: an organic compound that contains only carbon–carbon single bonds.

■ *e.g.* Alkanes are saturated; they take part in substitution reactions.

saturated fat: a type of fat that is usually hard at room temperature.

■ Many fats have fatty acids as part of the molecule. The composition of these affects the nature of the fat. The carbon atoms in the fatty acid part of saturated fats are linked by single bonds. Unsaturated fats have less hydrogen and some double bonds between the carbon atoms. There is a link between the amount of saturated fat in the diet and heart disease.

saturated solution: a solution that can hold no more solute at a particular temperature.

■ Solids generally become more soluble the higher the temperature of the solvent. Gases become less soluble the higher the temperature.

sea-floor spreading: widening of the sea floor that occurs where oceanic plates are moving apart.

■ Molten *basalt* wells up to fill the gap and then solidifies. Plates can move apart at speeds between 5 and 10 cm per year.

sea salt: a mixture of salts that has been obtained from sea water by evaporation.

■ The commonest component is sodium chloride; however, sea salt contains other salts including potassium chloride, bromide and iodide, and magnesium chloride and sulphate.

secretion: the process in which cells synthesise a desired substance, such as an enzyme, and pass it out of the cell.

■ *e.g.* Secreted substances include enzymes, hormones, mucus and sweat.

TIP Do not confuse secretion with *excretion*.

sedimentary rock: rock that has been weathered, transported by rivers and deposited in horizontal layers.

■ The particles within the layers are put under pressure by material deposited on top, and eventually the particles stick together by *cementation*. Sedimentary rock can contain the remains of plants and animals that have become trapped in the sediments in the past and have formed *fossils*.

■ *e.g.* Shale, sandstone and conglomerate are types of sedimentary rock.

seismic waves: shock waves caused by earthquakes, which travel through the Earth as *P waves* and *S waves*.

■ The study of these waves reveals the inner structure of the Earth.

seismograph: a device that records *seismic waves* so that they may be studied in detail.

S

selection pressure: a factor in the environment that affects the survival of individuals displaying particular features.

■ Selection pressures include living organisms, such as predators and food items, as well as physical factors including mean daily temperature and water availability. (See also *natural selection*.)

■ *e.g.* Low winter temperatures will select against animals that do not have thick insulation, and they survive less well. Organisms with good camouflage are more likely to evade predators.

selective breeding: the process of choosing individual plants or animals with good features as parents in order to produce offspring with desired combinations of these features.

■ This is used in animal and plant breeding to generate better varieties.

■ *e.g.* Parents can be chosen for features such as high milk yield, calmer temperament, whiter flowers or disease resistance.

series circuit: a circuit with components connected in series with no branching so that the same current flows through each component.

■ *Ammeters* should be connected in series.

> **TIP** In a series circuit, the component with the highest *resistance* has the largest *potential difference* across it.

sexual reproduction: reproduction involving the fusion of sex cells (*gametes*).

■ The offspring are genetically different from each other because each contains a unique combination of *alleles* (*genes*) from its parents.

■ *e.g.* The joining of a sperm with an egg.

sickle-cell anaemia: an inherited condition caused by a *recessive allele* that encodes a version of *haemoglobin* with a slightly changed structure arising from a *mutation* in *DNA*. This haemoglobin carries oxygen less well, and distorts the shape of red blood cells.

■ Individuals carrying one copy of the sickle-cell allele and one normal version (*heterozygotes*) make both normal and sickle-cell haemoglobin. Individuals with two copies of the allele suffer from the condition.

SI unit: a unit that belongs to the Système International d'Unités.

■ This coherent system of units is based on the metre, kilogram, second, *ampere*, Kelvin, candela and the *mole*. These units lead to derived units, such as the *newton* and the *joule*. There are also multiples and submultiples, such as kilo- and milli-.

skidding: the sliding of one surface on another when there is insufficient *friction*.

■ *e.g.* A car will skid if the effect of friction on the brakes is greater than the friction between the tyres and the road. A car will also skid when turning a corner too fast or too sharply if there is insufficient friction between the tyres and the road to *accelerate* the car sideways (change the direction of its motion).

slag: one of the waste products from a blast furnace.

■ In the manufacture of iron, the largest constituent of slag is calcium silicate ($CaSiO_3$), formed by the reaction of calcium oxide with silicon dioxide impurities in the haematite ore used. It is cooled, broken up and used either for road making or as an insulating material in houses.

slave piston: the piston that is pushed by the pressure in a *hydraulic system* in order to operate some piece of machinery.

TIP

The larger the diameter of the piston the larger the *force* produced.

slip rings: conducting rings on the *armature* of an *a.c. generator* which are joined to the rotating coil to pass the induced current to the fixed *brushes*.

smelting: the heating of a metallic ore in a furnace to produce the metal.

■ *e.g.* Oxide ores such as iron ore are often smelted with coke, which reduces the ore to metal and also provides heat for the process. Limestone is often added during smelting to help the ore to melt and to form a *slag*, removing many of the impurities present.

sodium hydroxide: a white, hygroscopic (water-absorbing) solid (NaOH).

■ It is strongly *alkali* and very corrosive. Sodium hydroxide is one of the products of the industrial electrolysis of sodium chloride. It is used to neutralise acids, in the manufacture of soap and in oven cleaners.

soft water: water that readily forms a lather with soap.

■ It does not contain calcium or magnesium salts which would react with soap and form a scum. (See also *hard water.*)

solar cell: a device that provides *renewable energy* by converting *light* energy into *electrical energy.*

■ Solar cells produce small voltages so many cells may be connected in a *series circuit*. As they are expensive they are mostly used in things like calculators where very little power is needed or in remote places and satellites where it would be difficult to provide electricity in any other way.

solar system: the Sun, together with all the *planets, comets* and *asteroids* that *orbit* it.

solder: the common name given to various *alloys* used for joining metals together.

■ Soft solders, alloys of tin and lead sometimes with added antimony, melt at low temperatures (about 200°C) and are widely used in the electrical industry. Hard (or brazing) solders melt at much higher temperatures and form much stronger joints. They are alloys of copper and tin. Brazing solders are used to join steel.

solid: a state of matter in which the particles touch but do not move over each other.

■ Solids are rigid, occupy a fixed volume and also a fixed shape.

solubility: the maximum mass of solid that will dissolve in 100g of solvent at any particular temperature.

■ *e.g.* At 20°C the solubility of copper sulphate is 21g per 100g of water.

solvent: a liquid that will dissolve solids.

■ The solid that dissolves is called the solute. A solute dissolved in a solvent is called a solution.

sound waves: *longitudinal waves* that travel relatively slowly in air but faster in solids.

■ Sound waves can be reflected by hard surfaces and diffracted around corners (see *reflection* and *diffraction*). The *frequencies* of sound waves range from 20 Hz (*wavelength* 16.5 m) to 20 kHz (wavelength 16.5 mm).

■ *e.g.* The speed of sound can be estimated by timing the interval between seeing a cricket ball being hit and hearing the sound. (See also *echo.*)

species: an interbreeding group of individuals that produce fertile offspring and which cannot interbreed with other groups.

■ Members of the same species have strong similarities in structure and metabolism, though there are small variations between individuals.

■ *e.g.* Dogs and foxes are different species. They have some similarities but cannot interbreed.

spectrum: see *electromagnetic spectrum* and *light.*

speed: the rate of movement, i.e. the distance travelled divided by the time taken.

■ Speed in m/s = distance in metres/time in seconds, $v = d/t$.

■ *e.g.* A girl runs 100 metres in 20 seconds, so her speed is 100 m/20 s = 5 m/s.

TIP
1 m/s is a little more than 2 miles/hour. Do not confuse speed, which tells you only 'how fast', with *velocity*, which tells you 'how fast and in what direction'.

speed of a wave: the speed in m/s equals the frequency in *hertz* × *wavelength* in metres, $v = f\lambda$.

TIP
To remember this, compare it to 'walking speed = number of steps per second × length of each step'.

speed/time graph (also called 'velocity/time graph'): a graph that shows the *speed* of an object, plotted vertically, against time plotted horizontally.

■ The gradient (slope) of the graph gives the *acceleration* and the area under the graph gives the distance travelled.

■ *e.g.* In the graph below, the acceleration in the first part is 8 m/s divided by 4 s = 8/4 m/s^2 = 2 m/s^2. The distance travelled is given by the area of the triangle, that is, $\frac{1}{2}$ (8 m/s × 4 s) = 16 m.

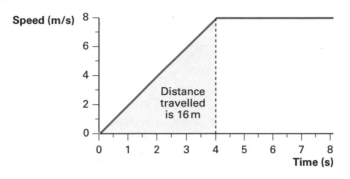

standard temperature and pressure: the conditions used when comparing the properties of gases.

■ Standard temperature is 0°C (273 K) and standard pressure is 100 kPa (100 000 N/m^2).

star: a sphere of matter held together by *gravity* and producing large amounts of electromagnetic radiation by means of *nuclear fusion.*

■ Our Sun is an average star out of many millions. Eventually it will become a *red giant.*

TIP

Stars produce light whereas *planets, moons* and *comets* only reflect light from the Sun.

starch: a carbohydrate that is a *polymer* of glucose, and the main insoluble energy store in plants.

■ Starch is broken down to soluble glucose by carbohydrate *enzymes* in the digestive systems of animals, as well as by plants themselves.

steel: an *alloy* of iron together with other elements (such as carbon and other metals).

■ *e.g.* Mild steel contains iron and up to 0.5% carbon. Stainless steel contains iron, nickel and chromium, and is resistant to corrosion. Tungsten steel contains iron and tungsten and is a hard steel used in cutting implements.

stimulus: something in the environment that causes a nervous impulse when perceived by the nervous system.

■ The stimulus is detected by receptors such as those in the eye, ear and skin.

■ *e.g.* Stimuli may also be internally generated, such as rising carbon dioxide levels in the blood leading to an increased rate of breathing.

stoma: a small opening in the surface of a leaf that allows gases in and out.

■ *Guard cells* by the openings (stomata) open or close them according to the

S

plant's needs. While there is sufficient light for *photosynthesis,* stomata are opened to allow carbon dioxide in, but they close when light intensity falls. Guard cells do this by changing shape.

stopping distance: the standard distance needed to stop a car going at a certain speed in good conditions.

■ It is the sum of the 'thinking distance' (the distance travelled while the driver reacts) and the 'braking distance' (the distance travelled while the brakes transform the *kinetic energy* of the car into *heat*).

■ *e.g.* The thinking time is taken as $\frac{2}{3}$ second; in this time the car goes 3 m for every 10 mph. The braking distance increases as the square of the speed. That means that at twice the speed, the braking distance is four times as great. The braking distance is also greater if the road is wet or if the brakes are in a poor condition.

stretching force: a *force* that pulls a wire or spring and puts it under *tension*.

■ The *extension* of a spring is proportional to the *tension*, provided the *elastic limit* is not exceeded.

strong acid: an acid that dissociates totally in an aqueous solution, producing a high concentration of H^+ ions.

■ Strong acids have a low *pH* value.

■ *e.g.* Hydrochloric (HCl), nitric (HNO_3) and sulphuric (H_2SO_4) acids.

sublimation: the change of state when a solid turns directly into a gas on heating, without going through the liquid stage.

■ *e.g.* Solid carbon dioxide and ammonium chloride sublime when heated.

substrate: any substance used up in a chemical reaction catalysed by enzymes or which is fed on by microbes.

sulphide: a compound of a metal or hydrogen with sulphur.

■ Sulphides occur in a number of minerals. The sulphur exists as the S^{2-} ion. The more volatile sulphides have very unpleasant odours (for example, hydrogen sulphide smells of bad eggs).

sulphuric acid: a strong, dibasic acid (H_2SO_4).

■ It is colourless but viscous in concentrated solution. Reactions of bases with sulphuric acid produce sulphates containing the SO_4^{2-} ion. Sulphur is burned in air to produce sulphur dioxide. The sulphur dioxide is mixed with more air and passed over a heated *catalyst* of vanadium(v) oxide. Sulphur trioxide is formed and dissolved in concentrated sulphuric acid to form a more concentrated solution. This can then be diluted to the strength of sulphuric acid required.

Sun: the *star* around which the Earth *orbits* and which provides most of our *renewable energy* and, in the past, produced all our *fossil fuels*.

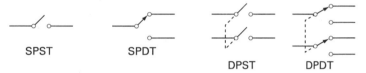

■ Sunlight enabled plants to grow and provide food for animals. When the plants and animals died many of them gradually turned into coal, oil and gas, to become our fossil fuels.

supernova: a large *red giant* that has contracted and exploded to become extremely bright for a short time.
■ A supernova throws off gas and dust and its remains become a *neutron star.*

survival of the fittest: see *natural selection.*

S wave: a *transverse* shock wave caused by an earthquake, which travels only through solids in the Earth. S waves travel more slowly than *P waves.*

switch: a device connected in series with an electrical circuit with contacts that *close* to allow current to flow and *open* to stop the current.
■ *e.g.* Common types of switch are:
• single pole single throw (SPST)
• single pole double throw (SPDT)
• double pole single throw (DPST)
• double pole double throw (DPDT)

SPST   SPDT   DPST   DPDT

The dashed lines show that both switches move together

symbiosis: see *mutualism.*

synapse: a minute gap between adjacent nerve cells.
■ The end of the axon of one *neurone* does not physically touch the next; they are separated by a synapse. When an impulse reaches the end of an axon, *neurotransmitter* molecules are released from the axon into the synapse. They diffuse across the gap and attach to receptors in the membrane of the next neurone. This triggers an impulse in the neurone.
■ *e.g.* Some painkillers work by blocking the passage of nerve impulses across the synapse linking sensory neurones to the brain.

syncline: a concave feature in folded sedimentary rock strata, usually formed as a result of surrounding plate movement.

Teflon (also called 'poly(tetrafluoroethene)'): a white *polymer* produced by the polymerisation of tetrafluoroethene.

■ Teflon is a thermosetting plastic with a high melting point which is used to produce non-stick surfaces on pans and to coat bearings to reduce the friction between them.

temperature: a measurement that describes how hot an object is, and how much *kinetic energy* its particles have.

■ Temperatures determine the direction of heat flow, which is from a higher temperature body to one at lower temperature. The common scales of temperature are degrees Celsius (°C) and Kelvin (K).

■ *e.g.* The freezing point of water is 0°C or 273 K. The boiling point of water is 100°C or 373 K.

temporary hardness: a form of hardness of water that can be removed by boiling.

■ Temporarily hard water contains dissolved calcium and magnesium hydrogen-carbonate. These cause soap to form a scum rather than a lather. Boiling the water precipitates out calcium or magnesium carbonate, thereby removing calcium and magnesium ions from solution. The water will no longer form a scum with soap.

tension: the *force* in a string or wire that is being pulled at both ends.

■ *e.g.* In the diagram below, the tension at the top is 10N since that is the force needed to stop the weight dropping. Remember that the tension each side of a pulley is the same.

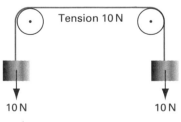

Tension 10 N

10 N   10 N

To work out the tension in a string, imagine cutting it and then discovering the force you would need on one of the cut ends to stop it moving.

terminal velocity: the steady *velocity* reached by a falling object when the upward *force* of air resistance has increased to be equal to the downward *weight* of the object.

- If you do not add that the direction of motion is 'down', you are really talking about the 'terminal speed'.
- *e.g.* If a sky diver in free fall is in a vertical standing position, he/she will go faster than when in a horizontal position. In each case the air resistance becomes equal to the sky diver's weight as he/she reaches terminal speed.

tests for ions: tests that allow the nature of the ions within a substance to be determined.

- They are usually based on chemical tests, although some metal compounds give specific colours when placed in a flame.
- *e.g.* Tests for negative ions:
  - halide (Cl^-, Br^-, I^-) ions give a precipitate with silver nitrate solution (chloride — white; bromide — pale yellow; iodide — yellow)
  - carbonate (CO_3^{2-}) — addition of a strong acid to a carbonate liberates carbon dioxide which turns lime-water milky
  - nitrate (NO_3^-) — sodium hydroxide solution and aluminium powder are added to a solution of the nitrate; the mixture is warmed and ammonia gas is produced which turns red litmus paper blue
  - sulphate (SO_4^{2-}) — addition of dilute hydrochloric acid and barium sulphate solution to a solution of a sulphate results in the immediate precipitation of barium sulphate

  Tests for positive ions:
  - ammonium (NH_4^+) — addition of sodium hydroxide to an ammonium compound, and warming, produces ammonia gas which turns red litmus paper blue
  - copper(II) (Cu^{2+}) — addition of sodium hydroxide solution produces a pale blue precipitate of copper hydroxide
  - iron(II) (Fe^{2+}) — addition of sodium hydroxide solution produces a blue-green precipitate of iron(II) hydroxide
  - iron(III) (Fe^{3+}) — addition of sodium hydroxide solution produces a brown precipitate of iron(III) hydroxide

thermistor (also called 'thermal resistor'): a resistor whose *resistance* decreases as its *temperature* increases.

- *e.g.* Thermistors can be used in electronic circuits that control temperature, for example to switch on a heater when the temperature falls or to switch on a refrigerator motor when the temperature rises.

t

tidal power: a *renewable energy* source of electrical power that comes from the up and down movement of the tides.

■ A dam is built across an estuary. As the tide rises, water moving into the estuary flows through turbines in the dam which generate electricity. As the tide falls, water moving out of the estuary again turns the turbines, generating more electricity. The motion of the Moon around the Earth causes the tides and this is the source of the energy.

■ *e.g.* There is a tidal power station in the Rance estuary near St Malo in northern France. The Severn estuary would be a good place for a tidal power station, but it would be very expensive to build and it would cause big changes to the estuary. For example, it could reduce the mudflats and so alter the complicated food webs and the plant and animal life in the estuary. However, the top of the dam, or barrage, would provide a useful road or rail link between the two sides of the estuary.

tide: see *Moon*.

tissue: a group of similar, specialised cells that carry out a particular job.

■ Organs such as the eye and the stomach, or parts of a plant such as a root or a leaf, are made of layers of tissues. Each tissue carries out a part of the function of the organ.

■ *e.g.* The tissues in a leaf make food for a plant: the epidermis keeps water in; the *palisade layer* carries out photosynthesis; the spongy layer carries out some photosynthesis and provides easy access for gases; *xylem* brings in water from the roots; and *phloem* takes away sugars and other substances made by photosynthesis to all living, non-photosynthetic cells in the plant, especially at growth points.

tissue typing: the identification of the *antigens* on a tissue. This is usually done in preparation for transplant surgery.

■ In organ transplants, the recipient and the donor must have the same antigens, or a very close match. If the donor's cells are different from the recipient's cells, the recipient's immune system will treat the transplanted tissues as it would invading microorganisms and try to destroy them.

titration: a technique used to find the concentration of one compound in a solution by determining how much of it will react with a known amount of another compound in solution.

■ One of the solutions is measured by a *pipette* into a conical flask. The other is added a little at a time from a *burette*. The completion of the reaction is determined with an indicator or an electrochemical device.

total internal reflection: the total *reflection* of a ray of light, or other wave, that is travelling from a dense medium toward a less-dense medium and making a small angle with the boundary. All the light is reflected at the boundary and none emerges from the other side.

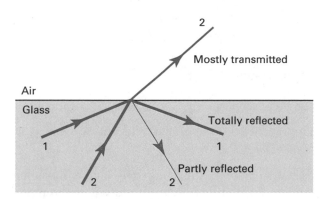

■ *e.g.* In an *optical fibre*, a ray of light travelling along the fibre might be totally reflected many times from the surface of the fibre, losing little of its energy while travelling a long distance.

toxin: any poisonous substance produced by an organism.

■ *e.g.* Toxins made by bacteria are responsible for many illnesses and are some of the most poisonous substances known. Many toxins are a defence against predators — some South American frogs secrete a toxin into the slimy coating over their skin. Local peoples use this frog toxin as an arrow poison for hunting. Many snakes produce at least one toxin, but in some cases there is so much that the prey is paralysed or killed when bitten. Some *fungi* also produce toxins.

trace elements: minerals required in very small quantities (milligrams or less) by living organisms.

■ Trace elements can be part of biologically important molecules. If there is a shortage of a trace element, part of the animal or plant's *metabolism* might be affected.

■ *e.g.* Magnesium is needed in plants for the *chlorophyll* molecule. Iodine is needed in humans to make thyroxine, a hormone produced by the thyroid gland.

transducer: a device that converts electrical signals into some other form of signal, or vice versa.

■ *e.g. Loudspeaker, microphone,* lamp, phototransistor.

transformer: an electrical device that changes the *voltage* and *current* of an *alternating current*, with little loss of *power*.

■ It consists of two coils that are wound around a soft iron core but are not connected to each other. The more turns on a coil the higher the voltage of that coil and the lower is the current in it, as shown by the formula:

$$\frac{\text{turns on the primary}}{\text{turns on the secondary}} = \frac{\text{primary voltage}}{\text{secondary voltage}} = \frac{\text{secondary current}}{\text{primary current}}$$

121

■ *e.g.* A transformer with 2000 turns on the primary needs to transform 240 V to 12 V. The number of turns on the secondary can be calculated from

$$\frac{2000 \text{ turns}}{\text{turns on the secondary}} = \frac{240 \text{ V}}{12 \text{ V}}$$

so that turns on the secondary $= \dfrac{12}{240} \times 2000 = 100$

If the secondary supplied 5A, the primary current would be 0.05A. (See also *electromagnetic induction*.)

transgenic animal: an animal with genes transplanted from another species.
■ The gene has to be transferred into the fertilised egg to pass into all of a developing animal's cells. Transgenic animals are useful for research, but potentially they could be sources of biologically important molecules that are difficult to obtain by conventional means.

transition metal: the name given to an element of the group positioned between groups 2 and 3 in the *periodic table*.
■ Transition metals have high melting and boiling points, variable *valency* and are able to form coloured compounds.
■ *e.g.* Iron, copper, chromium and manganese are common transition metals.

translocation: the movement of sugars and other materials through a plant.
■ Sugars travel through *phloem* cells up and down a plant. Sugar is translocated from the leaves, where it is made, to the roots for storage, to buds, shoots and flowers for growth, and to seeds and fruits for storage. The mechanism of translocation is not yet fully understood, but appears to involve *mass flow* in which sugar solution moves from an area where sugar is present in quantity (a 'source'), to a region where it is being used up (a 'sink').

TIP This is different from *transpiration*, which is a one-way movement of water.

transpiration: the loss of water by evaporation from a plant.
■ Water is distributed to photosynthesising tissues in leaves. Transpiration involves two processes. Water evaporates from mesophyll cells inside the leaf and then it diffuses out through the stomata. Water loss from the leaf pulls further water molecules from the xylem, creating a one-way flow through the plant. The water flow, called the transpiration stream, also carries minerals up from the roots.

transverse wave: a *wave* motion with particles that oscillate at right angles to the direction of motion of the wave.
■ *e.g.* Water moves up and down as a water wave travels along the surface. *Electromagnetic waves* and *S waves* in the Earth are also transverse waves.

trophic level: a feeding level in a food chain.

■ Organisms obtaining their energy by the same mode of nutrition in food chains and webs are at the same trophic level. Plants, which obtain food by *photosynthesis*, are the first trophic level. Herbivores, which feed on plants, are the second trophic level, intermediate carnivores are the third and so on.

turgid: the term used to describe plant cells that are swollen with water.

■ Plant cells rich in sugars and dissolved substances gain water from moist environments by *osmosis*. The vacuole reaches its maximum size and the cell contents push against the cell walls, bowing them outwards. Turgid cells push against each other, making the tissue firm and offering support to that part of the plant.

■ *e.g. Guard cells* around a *stoma* bend when they become turgid and open up a space between them that allows gas exchange.

ultrafiltration: a process in which fluid under high pressure is pushed through a membrane that filters out large molecules but lets small molecules pass.

■ *e.g.* Blood undergoes ultrafiltration in the kidneys. Blood under pressure enters the kidneys through the renal *artery*. The pressure increases as blood passes into smaller and smaller blood vessels. In the *glomerulus* plasma is forced through the capillary walls into the kidney tubule. Small dissolved molecules such as glucose and *urea* pass too, but larger protein molecules do not pass through and remain in the blood.

ultrasonic ranging: measuring distances by emitting pulses of *ultrasonic waves* and timing the return of *echoes.*

■ The method is similar to radar but, as sound waves travel much more slowly than *electromagnetic waves,* it can be used to measure small distances.

■ *e.g.* Autofocus cameras use it to measure the distance to the object being photographed, and estate agents might use it to measure the sizes of rooms.

ultrasonic waves: *longitudinal waves* similar to *sound waves* but having *frequencies* above the audible range.

■ *e.g.* These are used for imaging internal organs and body structures, for cleaning delicate instruments, for soldering aluminium and for machining hard, brittle materials.

ultraviolet: *electromagnetic waves* shorter than visible violet and longer than *X-rays.*

■ This radiation is more energetic than visible light and damages DNA, causing mutations. Much of it coming from the Sun is absorbed by *ozone* in the atmosphere.

unbalanced forces: forces that act on a body and, being unbalanced, mean that the body is not in *equilibrium* and is accelerated in the direction of the resultant force.

■ See *Newton's second law.*

unit (electrical): see *kilowatt hour.*

u

universe: all existing matter, energy and space.
- The universe could contain a billion *galaxies*, each of which could comprise a million *stars*. It is thought that the universe started with a *big bang* and has been expanding ever since.

unsaturated compound: an organic compound that contains one or more carbon–carbon *double bonds*.
- The test for an unsaturated compound is that it will decolorise bromine water.
- *e.g.* Alkenes — they take part in addition reactions.

unstable nucleus: the nucleus of an atom that will, at an unpredictable moment, emit *radiation* in the form of *alpha particles, beta particles* or *gamma rays*.

uranium dating: the dating of igneous rock by measuring the proportion of a radioactive uranium isotope to a lead isotope in the rock.
- The lead is stable and is the end product of a chain of radioactive *decay* that starts with the uranium. The older the rock, the lower the proportion of uranium there will be and therefore the higher the proportion of lead.

urea: a substance made when surplus *amino acids* are broken down in the body.
- Urea is made in the liver from surplus amino acids. The 'amino' part is turned into urea and passes into the bloodstream where it dissolves in plasma. It passes into kidney tubules when blood reaches the kidneys.

urine: a liquid produced by the kidneys and stored in the bladder.
- The composition of urine varies. When water is plentiful the kidneys make dilute urine. If water is in short supply, for example when a lot has been lost in sweating, a *hormone* (anti-diuretic hormone) changes the walls of the kidney tubules so that water is reabsorbed from the fluid in the tubules. This results in a smaller amount of more concentrated urine. Urine contains excreted *urea* made in the liver from *amino acid* breakdown and varying concentrations of sodium ions, depending on the concentration in the blood.

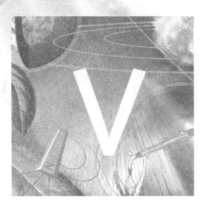

vaccination: a medical procedure that stimulates the body to make *antibodies* to a particular type of microorganism.

■ A solution of microorganisms or fragments of microbes is injected. It stimulates the *immune system* to make *antibodies* and memory cells against the micro-organism but does not cause the disease.

valence electron: an electron used by an atom to form ions or covalent bonds in a substance.

■ Valence electrons are those in the outermost electronic shell of an atom.

valency: the actual number of electrons used by an element to form ions or bonds.

■ The valency is usually the same as the number of electrons in the outermost shell, i.e. the group number. For an ion, the valency of the ion is the same as the charge on that ion.

■ *e.g.* Carbonate, CO_3^{2-}, has a valency of 2.

vapour: a gas that has evaporated from a liquid.

■ A vapour can usually be converted back to a liquid by *condensation*, or by applying pressure to the vapour.

variable resistor: a *resistor* whose *resistance* can be varied by sliding a contact along the resistor.

■ If there are two connections it is also called a *rheostat*. With three connections it is called a *potential divider* or potentiometer.

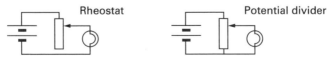

Rheostat   Potential divider

variation, continuous: differences in a feature, for example height, chlorophyll content of leaves, concentration of urea in urine or body mass, where there is a range of values between two extremes.

■ Features such as these may be influenced by the environment in which individuals grow, and also by the genes that they inherited from their parents. In good conditions, individuals might fulfil their genetic potential for, say, height, whereas in adverse conditions they might not. Some features exhibiting continuous variation are influenced by a number of different genes acting together.

variation, discontinuous: differences relating to two or more distinct categories, such as male or female, or free or fixed earlobes. There are no intermediate values. These characteristics are usually entirely genetic and not influenced by the environment.

vascular bundle: a cluster of transporting cells in the leaves and young stems of a plant.
- Each vascular bundle is composed of a cluster of *phloem* cells that carry sugars, cambium cells that divide to make new cells in the stem and *xylem* vessels that conduct water. The thick walls of xylem vessels give strength to the vascular bundle and help to support the plant.

vasoconstriction: the process of narrowing the diameter of blood vessels to reduce the amount of blood flowing into a tissue.
- Blood supply to the tissues is regulated according to the body's needs. Changes in the supply to the skin are important in regulating body temperature. Blood is warmed as it passes through the internal organs and muscles but loses heat as it passes through the skin.
- *e.g.* When the body is too cold, blood supply to the skin is reduced and so less heat is transferred to the environment.

vasodilation: the process of widening the diameter of blood vessels to increase the amount of blood flowing into a tissue
- *e.g.* When the body is too hot, *arteries* supplying the skin dilate, allowing more blood to pass through the surface tissues. This increases heat transfer to the environment.

TIP
Blood vessels do ***not*** move up or down in the skin with changing temperature.

vector: an agent that carries something from one location to another.
- Some infectious diseases are carried by vectors from one victim to another. In genetic modification, vectors are used to carry genes from one cell to another.
- *e.g.* Mosquitoes are vectors for the malaria parasite. The most common vectors used in genetic modification are plasmids, which are small pieces of DNA from bacteria.

vegetative propagation: the process of making more plants by *asexual reproduction*.
- Plants can reproduce asexually by making bulbs and corms, and by sending out stems that develop small plantlets at intervals. Horticulturists propagate

V

more plants by taking cuttings, splitting plants, dividing tubers and splitting bulb clusters.

vein: a blood vessel that returns blood to the heart.

■ Blood in veins has passed through the tissues and is at low pressure. Veins have thin but tough walls and valves to stop blood flowing backwards. Muscle action in the surrounding tissues helps move blood through veins.

velocity: *speed* in a given direction.

■ When giving a velocity you need to give both the speed and the direction, though the word 'velocity' is often used when 'speed' is meant. (See also *acceleration*.)

velocity/time graph: see *speed/time graph*.

ventilation: the movement of air or water across an exchange surface such as lungs or gills.

■ *e.g.* Air is moved in and out of the lungs by muscle action that results in a change of air pressure in the lungs. To inhale, the muscles of the ribcage and diaphragm contract. This lifts the ribcage and lowers the diaphragm, increasing the chest volume. In consequence the air pressure in the chest falls and air enters because of the higher pressure outside. To exhale, the ribcage muscles relax and the ribcage drops, and muscles in the diaphragm return it to its domed shape. This reduces the chest volume, increases the air pressure and forces air out.

vinegar: the common name for a 4% solution of ethanoic acid.

■ Vinegar is used to flavour food and as a preservative in pickling. Malt vinegar is brown and made from malted cereals. Cider, wine and honey can also be used in making vinegar.

virus: a minute infective agent, smaller than any bacteria.

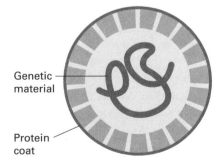

Genetic material

Protein coat

■ Viruses consist of a protein coat surrounding some genetic material. They can only reproduce inside living cells that they have infected.

volcano: a crack in the Earth's crust through which molten *magma* and gases come to the surface.

■ Most volcanoes are formed at plate boundaries, although some might form at localised hot-spots some distance away from the boundaries. Many, but not all, volcanoes are cone-shaped, formed from solidified material that has been ejected from the volcano, with a crater in the middle.

volt: the unit of *electromotive force* and *potential difference (p.d.)*, symbol V.
■ The p.d. across a resistor or other component is 1 volt when 1 *joule* of electrical energy is transformed for each *coulomb* that flows through the resistor.

voltage: a word used both for *electromotive force (e.m.f.)* and for *potential difference (p.d.)*.
■ There is an e.m.f. where *energy* is being converted **into** electricity and a p.d. where energy is being converted **from** electricity into some other form.

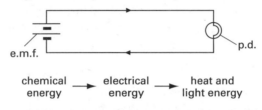

TIP

Although e.m.f. and p.d. have different meanings, which you should know, it is often convenient, and acceptable, to use voltage for both of them. But please don't use 'amperage' instead of 'current'.

voltmeter: a meter for measuring *voltage*. It may be *analogue* with a moving pointer or *digital* with a numerical display.
■ A voltmeter is connected in *parallel* and has a high *resistance* so that it causes little disturbance to the circuit. (See *parallel circuit*.)

TIP

When using one, do not break the circuit; simply connect the voltmeter across the *battery* or other component you wish to measure.

water cycle: the movement of water between the air, the land and the sea.
- Water in the sea evaporates and is condensed into clouds. Eventually the water falls as rain which is then returned to the sea by streams and run-off. The water cycle is powered by solar energy.

water potential: a measure of the concentration of water in a cell or tissue.
- It is used as a measure of the relative strength of a solution. Water moves from a region with a higher potential to a region with a lower potential.
- *e.g.* Something with a very low water potential, such as syrup, very salty water or a dried fruit will draw water from more dilute solutions. When dried fruit is placed in a bowl of water (high water potential), water will travel into the fruit by *osmosis*. The water potential of the blood is carefully regulated. Excess glucose or salt in the blood could cause cells to lose water to the bloodstream and be damaged.

water softener: a substance that removes calcium and magnesium compounds from water, thereby leaving the water soft and able to form a lather with soap.
- Calcium and magnesium ions can be removed by ion-exchange resins. They can also be removed by the addition of sodium carbonate, which precipitates them out as carbonates, leaving behind soluble sodium salts which do not cause hardness in water.

watt: a unit of *power*, symbol W, which is equal to 1 *joule* per second.
- Larger powers, especially electrical, are measured in kilowatts (1000 watts).

wave: a motion that moves forward and transmits energy by the oscillation of particles, which do not themselves move forward.
- In *longitudinal waves,* the particles oscillate in the direction of the wave's motion. In *transverse waves,* they oscillate at right angles to its motion. In *electromagnetic waves* there are no material particles but there are oscillating electric and magnetic fields.
- *e.g.* Water waves, *sound waves* and electromagnetic waves are all examples of wave motion.

wavelength: the distance between two crests of a wave. (See *amplitude*.)

weak acid: an acid that partially dissociates in aqueous solution, producing a low concentration of H^+ ions.
- Weak acids have a *pH* value close to 7.
- *e.g.* Ethanoic acid (CH_3CO_2H) and ethanedioic acid ($(CO_2H)_2$).

weathering: the process of breaking down rocks by exposure to the air and to the action of frost, rain and changes in temperature.
- These factors are partly physical (e.g. freeze and thaw of water in cracks opens them up as water expands on freezing) and partly chemical (see *acid rain*). Organisms also play a part in weathering (e.g. tree roots growing in cracks).

weight: the force with which an object is attracted downwards by the *gravitational field strength* of the earth.
- Although your *mass* may remain the same, your *weight* will be slightly greater at the poles than at the equator on account of differences in the gravitational field. If you move away from the Earth, your weight will keep decreasing but you will never become *weightless*. On the Moon your weight would be about one sixth of that on Earth; your mass would be the same.

weightless: a term used (wrongly) to describe astronauts who 'float about' inside a spacecraft. As they do not need to stand on the floor they are not aware of their *weight*.
- A spacecraft, an astronaut or any other object in *orbit* around the Earth needs a force towards the Earth to keep changing its direction of motion, even though its speed does not change (see *acceleration*). The weight of a spacecraft provides just the right force to keep it in its orbit; the weights of the astronauts provide just the right forces to keep them in the same orbit as the spacecraft. They all travel at the same speed and the astronauts can be inside or outside the spacecraft. The fact that they do not have to stand on the floor of the spacecraft means that they have no sensation of their own weight. However, if they and the spacecraft were suddenly to become truly weightless, they would travel into space at a steady speed along a straight path tangential to their original orbit.

white blood cell: a cell found in the blood that defends the body against infections and foreign material entering the body.
- There are several subgroups of white cells. One important group circulates in the blood and is found in the tissues. These cells take in particles of foreign material, such as bacteria and pollen, and destroy them. The other group is *lymphocytes*, which activate the response to infections and make *antibodies*.

white dwarf: a small star that has been a *red giant* but has used its fuel and contracted.
- Next it will become a *black dwarf.*

W

wind power: *renewable energy* produced by large windmills driving *generators*.

■ The source of the energy is the heating of the atmosphere, giving regions of high and low pressure which in turn cause winds. The energy is free but the construction of the windmill is expensive, and as the windmills are usually sited together in large 'wind farms', many people consider them unsightly.

work done: the *energy* converted from one form to another when a *force* moves.

■ Work done in joules = force in newtons × distance moved in the direction of the force in metres.

■ *e.g.* When a mass of 1kg is raised through a height of 4 m, the work done is equal to the force needed, 10N, multiplied by the vertical distance, 4 m. That is, 10N × 4 m = 40 J. This energy, the work done, is transferred to *gravitational potential energy* of the mass.

X-chromosome: one of two types of sex chromosome.
- In humans, women have two X-chromosomes. Men have one plus one *Y-chromosome*.

X-rays: *electromagnetic waves* that are shorter than *ultraviolet* rays and longer than *gamma rays*.
- X-rays cannot be focused as light can, so X-ray photographs are shadow photographs and are not as sharp as those taken with light. X-rays are more damaging than ultraviolet rays but are so useful in medical diagnosis that the possibility of a small amount of damage is acceptable. In scanners, X-rays and detectors are used with computers to generate very detailed images of the interior of a patient.

xylem: tissue consisting of cells specialised for transporting water through a plant.
- Xylem vessels lose their cytoplasm and have thick walls impregnated with waterproofing substances. The end walls between adjacent vessels may disappear to form long, strong tubes running up the stem. The strong walls play a part in supporting the plant. Xylem cells are clustered with *phloem* cells in *vascular bundles*.

Y-chromosome: see *X-chromosome*.

yeast: a microscopic, one-celled fungus used to make beer, wine and bread.
- Yeast cells convert sugar into carbon dioxide and alcohol by *anaerobic respiration*. Carbon dioxide gas causes bread dough to rise. In brewing and wine making, alcohol is the important product. Yeast cells are used as well as bacteria in *genetic modification* applications.

Zodiac: a belt of stars divided into the twelve constellations Aries, Taurus, Gemini, Cancer, Leo, Virgo, Libra, Scorpio, Sagittarius, Capricorn, Aquarius and Pisces.
- The zodiac forms a belt about 18° wide which is the background to the motions of the Sun, the Moon and most of the planets.

X Y Z

zygote: the cell formed by fertilisation when male and female *gametes* fuse.
■ Since gametes contain a half set of chromosomes, the zygote contains a new full set. The zygote divides repeatedly by *mitosis* to form the body cells of a new individual, which is genetically unique.